Organising for Safety

How structure creates culture

Organising for Safety
How structure creates culture

ANDREW HOPKINS

CCH AUSTRALIA LIMITED
GPO Box 4072, Sydney, NSW 2001
Head Office Macquarie Park
Phone: (02) 9857 1300 Fax: (02) 9857 1600
Customer Support
Phone: 1 300 300 224 Fax: 1 300 306 224
www.wolterskluwer.cch.com.au
Book Code: 35754A

Disclaimer

About Wolters Kluwer

Wolters Kluwer is a leading provider of accurate, authoritative and timely information services for professionals across the globe. We create value by combining information, deep expertise, and technology to provide our customers with solutions that contribute to the quality and effectiveness of their services. Professionals turn to us when they need actionable information to better serve their clients.

With the integrity and accuracy of over 45 years' experience in Australia and New Zealand, and over 175 years internationally, Wolters Kluwer is lifting the standard in software, knowledge, tools and education.

Wolters Kluwer – *When you have to be right.*

Enquiries are welcome on **1300 300 224**.

"Cataloguing-in-Publication Data available through the National Library of Australia."

First edition 2019

ISBN 9781925894158

Printed in Australia by McPherson's Printing Group

Forewords

"It has always been clear to me that culture change will not happen simply because the leader calls for it. As I have read this book it has increased my conviction that leaders who do want to change culture and improve risk management in their business must implement effective structural change which institutionalises the culture they strive for.

As ever, Andrew makes us think long and hard about what we say and what we do in practice. Real food for thought — and action — here".

Dame Judith Hackitt,
Former Chair of UK Health and Safety Executive,
Author of independent review for UK Government "Building Safer Futures"

"In the most, critical formative years of the U.S. Chemical Safety Board (CSB) one book stood out as essential reading for the organization — *Lessons from Longford*, by Andrew Hopkins. The book later provided the model for CSB's approach in investigating the 2005 BP Texas City Refinery disaster.

Organising for Safety is a timely addition to the list of must-read books by Hopkins. It includes valuable insights into a key question — what are we to make of the notion of safety culture?"

Bill Hoyle,
Retired Investigation Manager and Senior Investigator,
U.S. Chemical Safety Board

"*Organising for Safety* has provided the key 'missing link' for me in the High Reliability culture model. Our work has been focused at site level culture and leadership. I realize now that organization structure is critical to driving the right culture. I spent a month at the headquarters of

Corporation X pondering their organization and why it didn't seem 'right' to me, but I couldn't pin point or articulate it. Now, thanks to this book, I can. We will certainly be incorporating these ideas into our work with large oil companies striving to become High Reliability Organizations".

Bob Koonce

Commander, United States Navy (retired)
Founder, High Reliability Group LLC
Co-Author of *Extreme Operational Excellence: Applying the US Nuclear Submarine Culture to Your Organization*

Contents

About the Author

Andrew Hopkins is Emeritus Professor of Sociology at the Australian National University in Canberra.

He was an expert witness at the Royal Commission into the 1998 Exxon gas plant explosion near Melbourne. He was a consultant to the US Chemical Safety Board in its investigation of the BP Texas City Refinery disaster of 2005, and also for its investigation into the BP Gulf of Mexico oil spill of 2010. He has written books about all these accidents. More than 90,000 copies of his books have been sold.

He has been involved in various government Work, Health and Safety reviews and has done consultancy work for major companies in the mining, petroleum, chemical and electrical industries, as well as for Defence. He speaks regularly to audiences around the world about the human and organisational causes of major accidents.

He has a BSc and an MA from the Australian National University, a PhD from the University of Connecticut and is a Fellow of the Safety Institute of Australia.

He was the winner of the 2008 European Process Safety Centre safety award, the first in time it was awarded to someone outside Europe.

He is an honorary fellow of the Institution of Chemical Engineers in recognition of his "outstanding contributions to process safety and to the analysis of process safety related incidents".

Andrew can be contacted at andrew.hopkins@anu.edu.au

Books by Andrew Hopkins

Crime Law and Business: The Sociological Sources of Australian Monopoly Law (Australian Institute of Criminology, 1978)

Working for Change: The Movement Against Domestic Violence. With Heather McGregor (Allen and Unwin, 1991)

Making Safety Work (Allen & Unwin, 1995)

Managing Major Hazards: The Moura Mine Disaster (Allen & Unwin, 1999)

Lessons from Longford: The Esso Gas Plant Explosion (CCH, 2000)

Lessons from Longford: The Trial (CCH, 2002)

Safety, Culture and Risk (CCH, 2005)

Lessons from Gretley: Mindful Leadership and the Law (CCH, 2007)

Learning from High Reliability Organisations (CCH, 2009). Edited

Failure to Learn: the BP Texas City Refinery Disaster (CCH, 2009)

Disastrous Decisions: The Human and Organisational Causes of the Gulf of Mexico Blowout (CCH, 2012)

Nightmare Pipeline Failures: Fantasy Planning, Black Swans and Integrity Management (CCH 2014). With Jan Hayes

Risky Rewards: The Effect of Company Bonuses on Safety (Ashgate, London, 2015). With Sarah Maslen

Quiet Outrage: The Way of a Sociologist (CCH: Sydney, 2016)

Wolters Kluwer Acknowledgments

Wolters Kluwer wishes to thank the following who contributed to and supported this publication:

Regional Director, Research and Learning:	Lauren Ma
Head of Legal Content:	Carol Louw
Project Manager (Newgen):	Varshini Priya
Developmental Editor (Newgen):	George Yaksick
Sub Editor (Newgen):	Joyce Hemalatha Immanuel
Content Coordinator:	Nathan Grice
Cover Designer:	Mathias Johansson

Chapter 1
Introduction

How do we change the culture of an organisation? The dominant approach is best described by the 100th monkey parable. According to the parable, a single monkey on a certain Japanese island discovered how to wash the sweet potatoes it intended to eat. Other monkeys learnt the method by observation, and the number of monkeys behaving in this way grew until it reached 100. Thereafter, the new way spread like a contagion, even jumping to the next island by mind-to-mind transmission. Personal change gurus use this story as a model for how social change can be achieved: if some critical number of people change the way they think and act, the whole society will change.

Is this the best way to think about culture change in organisations? On the assumption that it is, books aimed at transforming the way individuals think are in high demand. Some of my previous books sold well because they could be used as educational resources in workshops aimed at bringing about culture change — one person at a time, or at least, small group by small group. This is the 100th monkey model in action, at least implicitly.

The present book cannot be used as an educational resource in this way because it is based on a radically different assumption about how culture change occurs. It takes the view that the culture of an organisation is determined to a large extent by its organisational structure. Changing the culture therefore requires a change in the structure. Moreover, it is ultimately the CEO who determines the organisational structure. If this book is to have any impact on cultures within organisations, it will need to be read by people at the very top of corporations, those who control their structures. So if you are not a CEO, there may be nothing you can do about this directly, other than recommending the book to your superiors, urging them to pass it up the line until it reaches people who do control the structure of your organisation. If you *are* a CEO, the book provides a practical guide to action. It offers a very different vision of culture change from that promoted by most culture change consultants. But I hope that after reading the book you will be persuaded, whoever you are.

The culture change industry tends not to talk about power.[1] In contrast, this book assumes that power and organisational culture are closely interrelated. The creation of a particular organisational structure is an exercise of power by the CEO and perhaps even the board of a company. In turn, that structure puts people into positions in which they can influence the culture of the organisation with respect to their areas of responsibility. In short, understanding an organisation's culture requires us to understand how power is distributed within the organisation. I shall not talk explicitly about power here, but the whole discussion could quite easily be framed in terms of power.

Structure, in this book, refers to the structure of positions, reporting lines and accountabilities, as summarised in the ubiquitous organisational chart. Of course, things are never quite as the charts represent because there are always personal connections that operate over and above the relationships depicted on the chart. Moreover, organisational structures are seldom static. They regularly change, depending on the needs of the organisation and the skills and capacities of the available people. Furthermore, most companies do not have comprehensive organisational charts setting out their structure in detail. The charts presented in this book have had to be pieced together from various documentary sources, supplemented by interviews. They are, therefore, at best approximations to the real structure.

A broader perspective

There is a broader context to all this. Structure suggests something that is relatively enduring and exists independently of the characteristics of individuals who inhabit the structure. It is part of a broader idea of "institutional arrangements" that exist independently of the individuals who make up the institution or organisation. The broader claim that can be made is that institutional arrangements determine culture to a large and perhaps surprising extent. Here are a few examples to make the point.

The commanding officer (CO) of an Australian Defence Force logistics and maintenance base was concerned about injuries occurring on the base. A significant proportion were occurring during physical training. The CO observed that the training culture was one in which people competed with each other, to the point of doing themselves injury. People were

---

1   Antonsen, S, Safety culture and the issue of power, *Safety Science* 2009, 47: 183–191.

required to do 25 push-ups but drove themselves to do as many as 90. They were expected to do route marches but drove themselves to finish as quickly as possible. The CO realised that one factor that contributed to the competitive culture was that the number of push-ups was recorded, as was the time taken to complete the route march. He directed that henceforth, all that would be recorded about push-ups was whether the individual had succeeded in performing the required 25. Furthermore, people would not be permitted to finish the route march in less than a specified time. This directive cleverly undermined the competitive culture that was proving injurious to the troops. It is a simple but dramatic example of the way cultures can be changed by altering the institutional arrangements that support them. It is particularly pertinent, given the problems of sporting and physical training injuries that plague the defence forces.

Second, a large construction company had a persistent problem of people working at heights without the required safety harness, despite repeated warnings. On investigation, it was discovered that the company had inadvertently created an incentive for non-compliance by setting in place a system in which people who finished their work first were given the first option on lucrative overtime work. When the company removed this incentive, the problem of non-compliance disappeared.

The third example may seem more esoteric. I include it to demonstrate the very broad relevance of these ideas. Spain is said to be plagued by a level of electoral corruption greater than is to be found in many other European democracies. This is sometimes explained as being an aspect of Spanish national culture. But as political scientists point out, there is what we might call an institutional reason for this high level of corruption.[2] In Spain, large numbers of government officials are political appointees and change when the government changes. They therefore have a vested interest in corrupting the electoral system to ensure that they remain in power. In countries where government officials are appointed on a merit basis and do not change when governments change, government institutions are less politicised and there is less corruption. In short, even a national culture may have institutional determinants.

As these examples demonstrate, the culture within an organisation cannot be understood in isolation from institutional or structural factors. Very

---

2   Victor Lapuente, *El País*, 27 March 2009.

often, in order to change a culture, we must remove the institutional support for the existing culture and put in place new arrangements that will support the desired culture. This book focuses on a particular aspect of the institutional arrangements of large organisations — their organisational structure.

Why this book?

I have written previously about the human and organisational causes of major accidents, such as coal mine explosions and oil refinery disasters. In every one of these accidents it turned out that organisational structure was a significant part of the explanation for the accident, arguably the most significant. In particular, in every one of these accidents, major hazards were being managed in a *decentralised* way, by local managers, rather than by the corporate centre. The degree to which major hazard risks are managed centrally turns out to be a critical variable in explaining major accidents.

There are good reasons for managing major hazard risks centrally. First, catastrophic events are rare. Individual sites such as coal mines and refineries may never have experienced a catastrophic accident, and site managers may not fully understand the risks. On the other hand, where the site is owned by a global corporation, that corporation has probably experienced a catastrophic event somewhere in its far flung operations. From a corporate point of view, these events are probably not unprecedented. Second, catastrophic events affect not only the local site, but the whole corporation; potentially, they can bring a corporation to its knees. Third, corporate headquarters can easily assemble the expertise to manage these risks effectively, while individual sites may not have the resources to do so.

Although I dealt with this question in previous books, I did not do it justice because those books were case studies, seeking to provide as full an explanation as possible for the particular case. The present book is not a single case study. It draws on many cases to demonstrate, in a more comprehensive way, the importance of centralised organisational control for the management of catastrophic risks.

Centralised control is important not only for the prevention of major accident events. It is important wherever the issue is one of vital significance for the corporation. Here is an example which at first sight appears frivolous, but which illustrates the point admirably. The McDonalds fast-food chain operates a *decentralised* model in many respects. The great majority of its outlets are independently owned franchises, responsible for their own profitability, indeed their own survival.[3] But the McDonalds corporation is vitally concerned about the quality and uniformity of the product provided — customers must be able to rely on being served the same product wherever in the world they may be. Quality control is therefore a central corporate function.[4] As this example makes clear, the principles discussed in this book are relevant to many large corporations. We shall see in due course that they apply in particular to the banking industry.

A petroleum industry focus

Much of my research and consultancy work has dealt with major accidents in the oil and gas industry. For this reason, and only for this reason, many of the examples here are drawn from the petroleum industry. I have also studied the mining and mineral processing industries which therefore provide a secondary source of examples for the book.

The term "process safety" is now widely used in the petroleum industry in relation to major hazard risks. This term will creep into my discussion occasionally so it needs to be explained here.

To begin with, industries that deal with major hazards need to distinguish carefully between, on the one hand, hazards that can cause catastrophic accidents involving major loss of life and major financial loss, and on the other hand, the hazards that cause more routine occupational accidents, which do not normally impact the organisation as a whole. This is clearest in the airline industry, where the crash of an airliner is clearly a catastrophic event, while an injury to a ground crew worker on the tarmac, even though fatal, is not catastrophic in the same sense. The safety challenges in these two cases are clearly of a different order.

This distinction is very relevant to the petroleum industry, which processes hazardous hydrocarbon fluids. At its simplest, process safety is about keeping hazardous substances properly contained in the pipes and tanks in which they are being processed. A loss of containment is a process safety event, because if there is an ignition source present, it can result in a major fire or explosion. The lesson that has painfully

---

3   www.corporate.mcdonalds.com/corpmcd/franchising/overview.html.

4   www.corporate.mcdonalds.com/corpmcd/scale-for-good/our-food/foodsafety.html.

emerged in recent decades for process industries is that, while personal or occupational safety can be appropriately managed in a decentralised way, process safety must be centrally managed. This has been most powerfully demonstrated by the experience of the petroleum company, BP. It has suffered two catastrophic accidents this century, each killing more than ten people, and each costing the company billions of dollars — the 2005 Texas City refinery explosion and the 2010 Gulf of Mexico oil well blowout. One of these accidents — the blowout — did enormous environmental damage and all but destroyed the fishing and tourism industries along the Gulf coast. BP's decentralised organisational structure contributed substantially to both these accidents. For this reason, BP figures prominently in this book.

Chapter outline

Investigation reports of major accidents often speak loosely of culture as a cause, while at the same time acknowledging that organisational factors play a major role. Chapter 2 is concerned with the interrelationship between organisational structure and culture. It draws on two major accident reports that clarify the relationship. These are, first, the report on the 2003 *Columbia* space shuttle accident that killed seven astronauts, and second, a report on a potentially catastrophic failure of America's tallest earth-fill dam, near San Francisco, in 2017. Both reports treat culture as a descriptive term — describing a state of affairs — "the way we do things around here". They go on to identify organisational structure as the primary determinant or cause of that culture, although they do so only implicitly. Both lead to the conclusion, therefore, that in an organisational context, *structure creates culture*.

This is a controversial proposition. Chapter 3, therefore, deals with some competing theories of how organisational cultures are created. These theories are as follows:

- cultures of safety can be created using educational workshops — the hearts and minds approach

- safety can be engineered using behaviorist methods — behaviour-based safety

- culture change is driven by the grass roots and spreads like a virus, and

- culture is created by leaders, by means of "felt leadership".

Each of these mechanisms is considered and discounted. None offers a real alternative to the claim that structure creates culture.

The views of safety theorists Erik Hollnagel and Sidney Dekker are also to some extent at odds with this thesis. Both advocate a position that can be described as safety anarchism. Chapter 4 argues that this philosophy has little relevance in the context of major hazards. In fact, it is potentially dangerous.

Chapter 5 is in many respects the heart of the book. It does two things. First, it is an extended account of the organisational change which BP underwent following its disastrous blowout in the Gulf of Mexico in 2010.[5] BP was transformed from perhaps the most decentralised of the major oil and gas companies, to the most centralised. In the view of its top management, this was the surest way to create the culture of process safety it needed to minimise the risk of future catastrophic accidents.

The second thing Chapter 5 does is introduce the theory needed to describe and understand BP's transformation. The reader will be introduced to the ideas about specialised functions, matrix organisation and the distinction between solid and dotted reporting lines. This material is introduced in the context of the BP case study to bring it to life as much as possible.

Chapter 6 continues this theme of what companies do after they have suffered a major accident. In 2010, the Canadian pipeline company, Enbridge, suffered a major rupture to one of its pipelines in the US state of Michigan. The rupture released a massive quantity of oily sludge that cost the company more than one billion dollars to clean up. Its organisational response was to create a stronger and more centralised structure to manage such risks. It did not go as far as BP, perhaps because its very existence was not threatened, as was BP's existence, but the transformation was a clear indication that the company saw structure as a key to changing its culture.

A second example is the case of BHP, following the catastrophic collapse of a tailings dam in Brazil in 2015. The collapse resulted in 17 deaths and the pollution of a river system all the way to the coast, hundreds of kilometres away. The accident cost BHP billions of dollars. The dam was part of a mining operation run by a subsidiary company called Samarco. This was a non-operated, joint venture (NOJV) — jointly owned with the Brazilian

---

5   Hopkins, A, *Disastrous Decision: The Human and Organisational Causes of the Gulf of Mexico Blowout*, Sydney, CCH Australia Limited, 2012.

mining company, Vale. Because it was non-operated, BHP (and Vale) did not monitor Samarco's operations closely. Following the accident, BHP set up an internal organisational unit to exercise much tighter control over all its tailings dams.

Chapter 7 shows how I have applied these ideas in particular cases in my own consultancy work. These cases include:

- the Australian Air Force, which experienced a health disaster affecting its aircraft maintenance workers

- a metalliferous mine which suffered a catastrophic cave-in

- a minerals processing company that was failing to manage process safety effectively, and

- a chemical company, whose safety assurance audits were being censored before reaching the board.

In each case, weaknesses in the organisational structure had allowed these things to occur, and in each case, I recommended organisational changes that would substantially reduce the risk of such events.

Chapter 8 is a case study of a particular company engaged in oil and gas production. It is based on PhD research by a process safety engineer. It contains three specific examples in which it is possible to demonstrate exactly how a decentralised organisational structure facilitated poor risk decisions, which in turn had demonstrably negative consequences. In each case, it is possible to show that these negative outcomes would almost certainly not have occurred in a more centralised structure.

All this raises the question of the nature of the evidence for the claim that organisational structure is the key explanatory variable. In particular, how can we be sure that strengthening the relevant parts of the organisational structure will indeed reduce the risk? Chapter 9 deals with this question. I conclude that we can never be sure, but that leaders cannot afford to wait until conclusive evidence is available. They face hazards with the potential to destroy their companies. They must therefore act on the basis of the best available evidence. And that evidence is persuasive.

If centralisation is the key to safety in hazardous industries, why is it that companies seem to wait until they have had a major scare before they act on this idea? Chapter 10 addresses this question by looking at structure in a broader context. Company priorities are set by CEOs, boards and remuneration systems. These are the ultimate determinants of organisational structure, and routinely they put short term profit ahead of effective risk management. The argument, here, draws on the well documented experience of the banking sector.

At this point in the discussion, the causal sequence of structure and culture is reversed. It is the culture of the board room that determines the structure of the organisation and how well it functions.

Chapter 11 offers a way forward. In the light of the previous analysis, what is it that companies need to do to manage risk more effectively? To answer this question, I introduce the idea of high-reliability organisations (HROs), organisations operating with hazardous technologies, but having many fewer accidents than might be expected. Their most distinctive feature is that they make great efforts to access and analyse the bad news about safety that exists at the grass roots in every organisation. The question therefore is: how can organisations ensure that they are accessing this bad news effectively? My proposal is that the company board should have a direct line of communication with the most senior risk or safety manager in the company and should remunerate that person on the basis of how well the organisation identifies and reports bad news and how effectively it responds. This would create an HRO champion at the top of the company. Chapter 11 provides a model for how this can be done.

Chapter 2
Structure creates culture

This book is about the crucial role of organisational structure in enhancing safety. However, there is a widespread competing view that what is critical for safety is the *culture* of an organisation, and in particular its *safety culture*. There is a pressing need for clarity about how these ideas relate to each other. To provide that clarity is one of the purposes of this book.

The problem comes into focus in the analysis of major accidents. Nowadays, many major accident reports speak of both organisational factors and a defective safety culture as causes of the accident in question. Unfortunately, they are seldom clear about the relationship between these things and the concept of culture seems to be grafted onto the analysis, rather than being a critical explanatory factor. This is exemplified by the various reports into the blowout on a drilling rig in the Gulf of Mexico in 2010. The rig, named the Deepwater Horizon, was under contract to BP, and it had just finished drilling the infamous "Macondo" well.

The first official report on the accident was by a specially constituted Presidential Commission of experts. It appeared just nine months after the disaster. It had much to say about organisational causes and it also used the language of culture and safety culture, for example in the following statement:

> The immediate causes of the Macondo well blowout can be traced to a series of identifiable mistakes made by BP, Halliburton, and Transocean that reveal such systematic failures in risk management that they place in doubt the safety culture of the entire industry.[1]

This passage appears to imply that the ultimate cause of the accident was the safety culture of the industry. However, much of the Commission's work was devoted to demonstrating that the accident was the result of an inadequate regulatory system, and that preventing such accidents required a different style of regulation. In reality, its reference to the safety culture of the industry is little more than a rhetorical flourish.

---

1 National Commission on the BP Deepwater Horizon Oil Spill and Offshore Drilling, *Deep Water: The Gulf Oil Disaster and the Future of Offshore Drilling*, 2011, p vii.

The second official report to appear was prepared by the Presidential Commission's Chief Counsel. It provided the material on which the Commission's report was based, in greater detail. Interestingly, this second report did not use the concept of safety culture at all. Whereas the President's Commission had spoken of a defective culture, the chief counsel spoke of "an overarching failure of management".

> The [Gulf of Mexico] disaster was not, as some have suggested, the result of a coincidental alignment of disparate technical failures. While many technical failures contributed to the blowout, the Chief Counsel's team traces each of them back to an overarching failure of management.[2]

The Commission itself acknowledges[3] that the Chief Counsel's report was far more comprehensive as to the causes of the accident than its own. Yet, the fact that the Chief Counsel was able to write his report without drawing on the concepts of culture or safety culture suggests that these were largely redundant concepts in the Commission's original report.

Finally, six years after the accident, by far the most extensive account was produced by an independent investigative agency, the US Chemical Safety Board. Neither culture nor safety culture was a key concept in this four-volume report. In fact, safety culture is the subject of one brief chapter in volume 3. This is largely a critique of safety culture surveys conducted prior to the accident by BP and Transocean, the owner of the rig. It is an add-on to the Board's analysis, not a central feature of it.

These various reports demonstrate a pervasive ambivalence about the explanatory value of the notions of culture and safety culture. For the most part, these terms are used in summary statements, but they seem not to be an integral part of the analysis.

There is, however, at least one prominent major accident report that does make systematic and considered use of the concept of culture. Moreover, as we shall see in what follows, this report provides the key to integrating the concepts of structure and culture.

---

2   National Commission on the BP Deepwater Horizon Oil Spill and Offshore Drilling, Chief Counsel's Report, *Macondo: The Gulf Oil Disaster*, 2011, p 225.

3   Op cit, p ix.

Structure creates culture

The *Columbia* Accident Investigation Board Report

In 2003, the *Columbia* space shuttle disintegrated on re-entering the earth's atmosphere, killing the seven people on board. Culture was a key concept for the accident investigation board, perhaps because one of the Board members was a sociologist who had written a very influential book about the previous *Challenger* shuttle accident of 1986 in which another seven astronauts had died. That book used the culture of the US National Aeronautical and Space Administration (NASA) as an explanatory concept. So, it was to be expected that the *Columbia* investigation would do likewise. Accordingly, we find the following statement in the report by the *Columbia* Accident Investigation Board.

> In the Board's view, NASA's organisational culture and structure had as much to do with this accident as the [physical causes]. Organisational culture refers to the values, norms, beliefs, and practices that govern how an institution functions. At the most basic level, organisational culture defines the assumptions that employees make as they carry out their work. It is a powerful force that can persist through reorganisations and the reassignment of key personnel.[4]

The Board was even more specific: it described NASA's "flawed" or "broken" safety culture as one of the primary organisational causes of the accident.[5]

Given this analysis, the Board's recommendations are necessarily about fixing the culture. This makes it a particular interesting case from the present point of view. How did they envisage that the culture might be fixed?

To answer this question, we must go into the Board's analysis in greater detail. The prevailing NASA culture was one in which the paramount goals were cost minimisation and keeping to schedule. The potential for safety to be sacrificed in pursuit of these goals is obvious. NASA's slogan was "faster, better, cheaper."[6] "Better" might conceivably have encompassed safety, but in practice it didn't. In an effort to ensure safety was not overlooked, NASA had set up various safety and mission assurance organisational sub-units

---

4   The Columbia Accident Investigation Board (CAIB) Report, p 97.

5   Op cit, pp 184, 189.

6   The Columbia Accident Investigation Board (CAIB) Report, p 199.

within the larger organisational whole. But these were not sufficiently independent of line managers, they were starved of funds and they were not strong enough to act as a counterweight to the dominant culture of "faster, better, cheaper". The Board's recommendations were designed to rectify this, in particular, by setting up a powerful counterweight, a Technical Engineering Authority, at the top of the organisation. The aim of this Authority was to ensure that safety was not overridden by other organisational goals.

I reproduce that recommendation here in detail because of its importance and because I shall refer back to it later.[7]

Box 2.1: The *Columbia* Accident Investigation Board's principal recommendation to fix the broken safety culture

Establish an independent Technical Engineering Authority that is responsible for technical requirements and all waivers to them, and will build a disciplined, systematic approach to identifying, analyzing, and controlling hazards throughout the life cycle of the Shuttle System. The independent technical authority does the following as a minimum:

- Develop and maintain technical standards for all Space Shuttle Program projects and elements

- Be the sole waiver-granting authority for all technical standards

- Conduct trend and risk analysis at the subsystem, system, and enterprise levels

- Own the failure mode, effects analysis and hazard reporting systems

- Conduct integrated hazard analysis

- Decide what is and is not an anomalous event

- Independently verify launch readiness

- ....

---

7   Op cit, p 193.

> The Technical Engineering Authority should be funded directly from NASA Headquarters, and should have no connection to or responsibility for schedule or program cost.

Certain features of this recommendation are worth highlighting. The second specific function — to be the sole waiver-granting authority for all technical standards — is a response to the fact that existing authorities in NASA were too easily waiving standards that stood in the way of "faster, better, cheaper". This is a potential problem in all large organisations dealing with hazardous processes about which I will have more to say later.

The second last of these specific functions — decide what is and is not an anomalous event — is intended to overcome NASA's tendency to *normalise* unintended or anomalous events, or to risk-assess them as insignificant. In the *Columbia* case, chunks of foam had broken off the external tank at launch on many previous occasions and hit the shuttle, denting it, with no adverse consequences. Though indicative of a design failure, this came to be seen as acceptable. On the occasion of the fatal launch, a larger than normal piece had broken off and struck the leading edge of the shuttle's wing, creating a hole that caused the shuttle to disintegrate on re-entry. Had these anomalous events not been normalised and accepted, the accident would not have occurred.

The last item in the above list — independent verification of launch readiness — is designed to guard against launch decisions driven by schedule and cost, rather than safety. The *Challenger* launch decision would not have been made, if independent verification of launch readiness had been required.

The recommendation in relation to funding is in part to ensure that the Technical Engineering Authority has no financial interest in authorizing a launch against its better judgement.[8]

What is most interesting about the recommendation to establish a Technical Engineering Authority is that it is first and foremost a recommendation

---

8   In an attempt to bring together and empower the mission assurance program, the Board made a second recommendation as follows (CAIB, p 193):

NASA Headquarters Office of Safety and Mission Assurance should have direct line authority over the entire Space Shuttle Program safety organisation and should be independently resourced.

This is analogous to the TEA recommendations will not be discussed here.

about organisational structure. There is no suggestion here that the cultural problem the Board has identified permits of a cultural solution, whatever that might mean. Rather, the solution lies in the area of organisational structure. The *existing* organisational structure has allowed NASA to operate with a defective safety culture and the *proposed* organisational structure would force NASA to give safety a greater priority in everything it did. The assumption is that *structure creates culture*. This is a principle we shall encounter often in this book.

The US nuclear submarine organisation

It is noteworthy that the *Columbia* Board, and indeed NASA, looked to the US nuclear submarine organisation for guidance on how to fix the NASA culture.[9] The Navy lost an average of one submarine every three years from 1915 to 1963.[10] The last in this series was the first involving a nuclear-powered submarine.[11] The Navy reacted resolutely and set up a system that has seen no further losses, with one partial exception.[12] The essence of the Navy's program is that technical engineering, and other matters of mission safety assurance, are the responsibility of independent authorities, with no responsibility for cost, schedules, or other operational considerations.[13] Here is how the *Columbia* Board put it:

> The practices [of the US nuclear submarine program, among others] suggest that responsibility and authority for decisions involving technical requirements and safety should rest with an independent technical authority. Organisations that successfully operate high-risk technologies have a major characteristic in common: they place a premium on safety and reliability by structuring their programs so that technical and safety engineering organisations own the process of determining, maintaining, and waiving technical requirements with a voice that is equal to yet independent of Program Managers, who are governed by cost, schedule and mission-accomplishment goals. The Naval Reactors Program, SUBSAFE program, and the Aerospace

---

9   The Columbia Accident Investigation Board (CAIB) Report, pp 182–184.

10 Leveson, N, *Engineering a Safer World: Systems Thinking Applied to Safety*, Draft of July 2009, p 377.

11 USS Thresher.

12 USS Scorpion.

13 For a recent account, see Digeronimo, M and Koonce, B, *Extreme Operational Excellence*, 2016, Outskirts Press.

Corporation are examples of organisations that have invested in redundant technical authorities and processes to become highly reliable.

Clearly, the *Columbia* Board was highly influenced by the nuclear navy model. NASA was less influenced, as will be apparent in the following section.

A sequel to the Columbia Accident Investigation Board

NASA accepted the recommendations of the *Columbia* Board, in principle.[14] However, the practice turned out to be a little different. The US Government Accountability Office (GAO) revisited the issue of NASA's organisational structure in 2017 and expressed great concern about what it called "dual hatting".[15] Certain engineers were designated by the Technical Engineering Authority as the "technical authorities" (TAs) for particular sub-engineering disciplines. Their job was to ensure that standards were maintained. But the same people also played a role in engineering development work and were responsible for managing the budgets allocated for this work. This undermined their capacity to perform the role envisaged by the Board in counteracting budget and schedule pressures. As the GAO report put it, having dual hats means these individuals are responsible for "grading their own homework".

NASA rejected this criticism on various grounds. First, it argued that it would not be an efficient use of resources to have an independent technical authority with no program (line) responsibilities. In doing so, it was essentially rejecting the original advice of the *Columbia* Board, which had identified this lack of independent verification as the root of the problem.

Second, NASA argued that it had filled the positions with the right people — people with sufficient technical competence to perform both roles. This is an argument that is often made by top managers when they do not want to make recommended structural changes. It is based on the belief that having the right people in the job is the most important requirement for achieving the right outcome. It discounts entirely the issue of conflict of

---

14 Office of the Chief Engineer, *NASA Space Flight Program and Project Management Handbook*, 2014. See especially pp 237–263. See also www.nasa.gov/offices/oce/functions/tech_auth.html.

15 United States Government Accountability Office, *NASA Human Space Exploration: Integration Approach Presents Challenges to Oversight and Independence*, October 2017.

interest and the pressures that can be placed on the "right" people to do the "wrong" thing.

Third, NASA argued that the primary reporting lines for these TAs were to higher managers in the Technical Engineering Authority, not to program (line) managers. At first sight this is a plausible argument, except that, in the NASA context, it suffers from a fundamental weakness. Dual-hatted individuals are also responsible to higher line managers for managing budgets. This inevitably compromises their ability to act independently.

The GAO was unpersuaded by NASA's responses. It concluded that NASA had not adequately dealt with the conflict of interest inherent in its dual-hat approach and that this organisational structure was not consistent with the recommendations of the *Columbia* Board. If there is another space disaster in the years to come, NASA's failure to follow the recommendations of the Board will likely be identified as a root cause.

Culture as description

What, then, is the status of the concept of culture in the *Columbia* report? It is not an independent cause, but rather a consequence of a more fundamental cause — organisational structure. But if culture is not the cause in this context, what is it? In my view it is best viewed as a *description*. Here I must finally get precise about the meaning of culture. Among the many meanings that academics have produced,[16] the one that stands out as most concrete and most useful is — "the way we do things around here". If we routinely normalise or ignore discrepant events, and routinely deviate from engineering standards or from required procedures because it is cheaper or more convenient to do so, this *way of doing things* amounts to an unsafe culture. On the other hand, if we routinely report anomalies and stop the process until they are resolved, and in addition we comply strictly with procedures and standards, this is truly a culture of safety.

---

16 Schein, E, *Organisational Culture and Leadership*, San Francisco, Josey-Bass, 1992 provides an extensive list.

Description and explanation are clearly two different things. If culture describes a certain state of affairs, it cannot also serve as an explanation for that state of affairs. We must look further afield to understand why things are as they are. In organisational contexts, that explanation will be found in large part by examining the organisational structure.

There is one context in which it is appropriate to identify culture as cause. That is when we are talking about the cause of individual behavior. Individuals in groups often feel constrained by the culture of the group to behave in a certain way, that is, to conform to "the way we do things around here". If none of my workmates wears a safety harness when working at heights, despite the written procedure requiring this, then it is difficult for me to go against the group practice and comply with the procedure. Here, culture becomes an explanation for my behaviour. But it is also a description of the group's behavior, which itself requires explanation, in terms of a lack of supervision by a higher-level manager, and so on. This leads us directly back to organisational causes.

Qualifying the claim

At this point, in order to avoid confusion, I need to qualify the claim that structure creates culture. First, while a centrally driven structure of independent technical assurance can create a particular culture, the lack of such a structure does not automatically generate any particular alternative. Rather, it leaves the way open for other factors to influence the culture of the organisation. So, at NASA, the lack of independent technical assurance allowed the culture of "faster, better, cheaper" to prevail. This was a culture driven by NASA leadership in response to external political imperatives.

Second, the claim refers to the source of *organisational* culture. The cultures of peer groups, professional groups and the nation, for example, must be analysed differently. They are influenced by the media, education, religion, and so on.

Third, structure will only determine culture if positions specified in organisational charts are occupied by people with the requisite competence. If leaders fail to resource appropriately the structure they have created, it will not have the desired effect.

Fourth, the beneficial impact of a particular organisational structure can be undermined if the organisation establishes perverse financial incentives. This will be dealt with at some length in Chapter 10.

These qualifications are listed here for completeness, but for the most part they are taken for granted in my discussion.

The near failure of America's tallest earth-filled dam

It is worth providing a second example of a report on a major incident that uses the concept of an "immature" or inadequate safety culture to describe the problem, but then identifies specific changes to organisational structure to remedy the problem. I provide this example because it is recent, and also because it deals with a rather different type of catastrophic scenario — the failure of a large water storage dam with the potential to kill thousands of people downstream.

On February 12, 2017, nearly 200,000 residents downstream from the dam were ordered to evacuate their homes and move to higher ground. Yes, 200,000! It is hard to imagine the extent of this dislocation. Residents were told that a wall of water 30 feet high could be headed their way.[17] The dam is at Oroville, north of San Francisco. Its level was rising due to heavy, but not unprecedented rain in the catchment. Nevertheless, the emergency spillway was "expected" to fail, resulting possibly in an "uncontrolled release of flood waters."[18] Hence the evacuation order. As it turned out, the spillway failure was averted, and the order was lifted two days later.

The dam had not one, but two spillways. See Figures 2.1, 2.2. The first, a service spillway, was designed to discharge water safely during routine flood events such as occurred on this occasion. It consisted of a concrete channel or chute, off to the side of the main dam wall, taking water to the valley floor below the dam, in a controlled fashion. The second, an

---

17   www.nbcnews.com/news/us-news/one-year-later-oroville-dam-crisis-still-weighs-residents-minds-n846021.

18   *Los Angeles Times*, 12 February 2017.

emergency spillway, with a slightly higher crest, was located a little further away. It had no concrete lining down into the valley and discharged into a natural water course. It was intended to come into action only if the service spillway could not be used. This emergency spillway had never been used in the 50 years of the dam's existence.

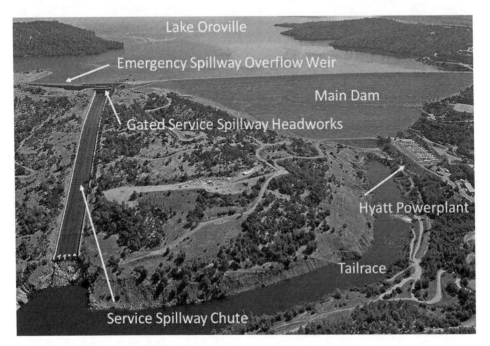

Figure 2.1: Oroville dam, showing main features. Moving from left to right across the top of the picture, one can see the emergency spillway, the service spillway and the main dam wall[19]

19   Source: Independent Forensic Team Report, *Oroville Dam Spillway Incident*, January 2018, p 8.

Figure 2.2: Oroville dam showing service spillway in use and extensivly
damaged in the lower section[20]

The service spillway had been damaged during earlier overflow events,
and repaired on several occasions, but never satisfactorily. However,
on this occasion the damage was greater, and the concrete lining of the
spillway was threatening to disintegrate. There was no question of the
dam wall itself giving way, but if the concrete spillway was washed
away, erosion in the newly exposed water course would be substantial,
and displaced material could damage infrastructure downstream. The
decision was therefore made to close the gates at the top of the service
spillway, partially, and allow the water level to rise and overflow the via

20   Source: Josh Edelson.

the emergency spillway. Certain engineers advised that this was risky because of the known limitations with the emergency spillway, but they were overridden (see below). Once the water began to flow over the crest of the emergency spillway, the water course below this spillway began to erode rapidly, which threatened to destroy the spillway crest above, causing a catastrophic breach of containment of the emergency spillway. At this point, the authorities had no option but to issue an evacuation order. The dam management responded to this crisis by opening the gates of the *service* spillway further, which reduced the flow down the *emergency* spillway. By so doing they managed to avoid a catastrophic breach in the crest of the emergency spillway, but at the cost of increased damage to the service spillway.

Dams should be designed and managed to avoid such catastrophic possibilities. How, then, could this dam have come so close to failure?

An independent report into the causes of this incident placed considerable emphasis on the idea of an inadequate dam safety culture within the California Department of Water Resources (DWR) that owned and operated the dam. The report noted that "the dam safety culture and program within the DWR, although maturing rapidly and on the right path, was still relatively immature at the time of the incident".[21]

In coming to this conclusion, the report team used a five-step maturity scale designed to assess dam owners. The categories, from most to least mature, are as follows:

- leading edge
- best practice
- good industry practice
- intermediate, and
- needing development.

---

21 Independent Forensic Team Report, *Oroville Dam Spillway Incident*, January 2018, p S2.

This scale, in itself, deserves some comment. The top three categories all provide dam owners with a pat on the back. The label "intermediate" implies a somewhat neutral evaluation and one might have expected it to be used for the middle category, but in fact it is applied to the second bottom.

Only the very bottom category, "needing development", carries a negative connotation and then only the very mildest. Clearly, the designers of this scale were intent on minimising any offence that the use of this scale might give to dam owners.

The report team evaluated the owner of the Oroville dam on a range of criteria. On one criterion, the evaluation was the middle category (good practice) but on all the others, it was either the lowest or second lowest ranking.[22] This is the basis of the team's comment that the "dam safety culture ... was relatively immature at the time of the incident", although in truth the results would have justified a rather harsher conclusion.

Corresponding to this evaluation, one of the main lessons the report identified was that "dam owners must develop and maintain mature dam safety management programs which are based on a strong top-down dam safety culture."[23]

How did they propose that this top-down safety culture be developed? In fact, the report's most important recommendations in this respect were based on an analysis of the organisational structure and its consequences. The team drew up a detailed organisational chart, from which Figure 2.3 is extracted.[24]

---

22   Op cit, p K1-25.
23   Op cit, p S3.
24   Op cit, p K1-22.

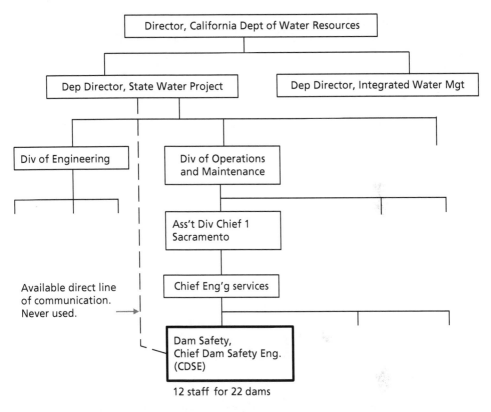

Figure 2.3: Portion of organisational chart showing position of chief dam safety engineer

There are two lines of interest in this diagram — the Division of Engineering and the Division of Operations and Maintenance. The Department viewed the Division of Operations and Maintenance as the "owner" of its dams, while the Division of Engineering was seen as a service provider. Dam safety was recognised as an owner's responsibility, so it was located within the Division of Operations and Maintenance (text box with heavy border). The engineers who had warned against using the emergency spillway sat within the Division of Engineering. They were therefore not on the dam owner's "team", which undermined their influence in the crisis.

The Chief Dam Safety Engineer (CDSE) is potentially the most important person in the whole organisation from a dam safety point of view. A powerful CDSE would have been in a position to insist that the dam owner fix the problem of the defective service spillway once and for all, long before the events of February 2017. A powerful CDSE would also have been better able to argue against the deliberate use of the emergency spillway which was known to be problematic. But as can be seen from the organisational chart, the CDSE was anything but powerful. As the report observes, the CDSE was four layers down from the relevant deputy director. As if in recognition of this problem, there was, theoretically, a direct line of communication available between the CDSE and the deputy director (dotted line on chart), but this had never been used by either party. The CDSE was thus completely isolated from the higher echelons of the organisation and was bypassed in many decision-making processes.[25] Moreover, many of his previous recommendations for the investigation of observed anomalies were never actioned by higher level managers.[26] The report argues that the Department should build the capacity of the dam safety engineers within the organisation to speak with "a loud voice" to management.[27]

One reason why the position of Chief Dam Safety Engineer is so important is that there is an inherent tension between dam safety and production activity (water supply and hydroelectricity generation). Inevitably, trade-offs must be made between these two goals. This is explicitly recognised by the International Committee on Large Dams,[28] which argues that whoever is responsible for overseeing dam safety must be sufficiently senior to ensure that these trade-offs are being managed properly. It is clear, the report says, that the Chief Dam Safety Engineer was not in such a position.

The report also noted that nearly all the senior positions in the Department of Water Resources required managerial expertise, not technical expertise, and that the capacity of the senior people to understand the critical nature of technical issues was limited.[29]

The report makes two main recommendations about this situation. First,

- there should be a particular manager at the executive level [deputy director level — see Figure 2.3] with specific responsibility for dam

---

25   pK 1–14.
26   pK 1–9.
27   pK 1–15.
28   pK 1–14.
29   P 69.

safety and for managing the trade-off between dam safety and production.

The report does not specify that this person be technically trained, but it notes that such training is envisaged by the International Committee on Large Dams.[30]

This recommendation was subsequently implemented when the Department appointed a deputy director specifically responsible for dam safety and flood management.[31] As can be seen in Figure 2.3, deputy directors report to the director, that is the CEO of the organisation. Organisations that have been sufficiently shaken by an incident frequently respond by creating a safety position answering to the CEO in this way.

The second recommendation was that:

- the Chief Dam Safety Engineer should report directly to the member of the executive identified above. This would elevate the position of CDSE several steps in the organisational hierarchy. The position would also need much better resourcing.

It is not clear whether this recommendation was implemented.

The most important thing to note here, however, is that the report on the Oroville Dam incident recommends a change in the *organisational structure* as the means of creating a "strong top-down dam *safety culture*". In short, it, too, endorses the idea that in an organisational context, *structure creates culture*.

The culture of on-time running

The idea that structure creates culture is such an important insight that I shall illustrate it with a quite different kind of culture — the culture of on-time running that exists in many railways. This came to prominence during an inquiry into a rail crash at Glenbrook near Sydney in 1999.[32] The inquiry found that one of the causes of the accident was its culture of on-time running, or punctuality, which meant that trains were travelling faster than they should have been, in order to make up for lost time.

---

30 pK 1–7.

31 www.latimes.com/local/california/la-me-water-chief-ouster-20180110-story.html.

32 See Hopkins, A, *Safety Culture and Risk*, Sydney, CCH, 2005, Part B.

It is worth examining the culture of on-time running in its own right. It consisted of a set of practices which involved people at all levels. These practices included detailed monitoring of driver performance to ensure that trains arrived at their destinations within three minutes of their scheduled arrival time. Importantly, there were sanctions of various sorts against drivers who failed to meet schedules. All this involved a massive organisational apparatus, with large numbers of people whose sole job was to ensure that trains ran on time. It was this organisational apparatus that ensured the pre-eminence of the culture of on-time running. It is clear that when outcomes are important enough, organisations will structure themselves so as to achieve these outcomes.

This raises the question of why punctuality is such an imperative for train company managers. The answer is that there is enormous pressure — public, political and regulatory — to run on time. Often, there are financial penalties for failure to run on time. That is why train companies *organise* themselves to create a *culture* of on-time running. Ultimately, it is often the external environment that determines what is really important for the organisation, and hence the way it is structured.

Conclusion

There is much loose talk about culture in discussions of safety. I take culture to be "the way we do things around here". (This definition will be elaborated in Chapter 3.) A culture of safety, therefore, is a way of doing things that emphasises safety. How can such a culture be achieved? By developing organisational structures that give priority to safety. This is the conclusion of major accident reports that have taken the notion of culture seriously and crafted recommendations designed to achieve a culture of safety. The principle is that structure creates culture, a principle that covers many aspects of organisational life, as diverse as punctuality, in the case of train companies. In the following chapter, I consider contrasting views about how cultures of safety may be created, but as we shall see, none challenges this basic proposition.

In later chapters, the concept of culture will tend to slip into the background, since the desired end state is safe operation, and a culture of safety is simply a means to that end. The focus will be on designing the most appropriate organisational structure to achieve operational safety.

Chapter 3

Alternatives to the structuralist approach

The structuralist approach to achieving a culture of safety runs counter to several other popular approaches. We pause here to take stock of these alternatives, identifying the differences as well as points of convergence. Either explicitly or implicitly, the starting point for all these approaches is that culture is a descriptive term — a term that describes a state of affairs that is either current, or desired. Each approach then advocates a particular way in which the desired culture can be achieved. The following approaches will be discussed in this chapter:

- cultures of safety can be created using educational workshops — the hearts and minds approach,

- safety can be engineered using behaviorist methods — behaviour-based safety,

- culture change is driven by the grass roots and spreads like a virus, and

- culture is created by leaders — felt leadership.

These approaches are championed by a variety of consultants and consulting academics who collectively make up what can be called a culture change industry.[1] Many of these people mention structural change only in passing, if at all, because the structural approach is for them an existential threat. If culture change depends on changing organisational structures, then all their efforts to promote culture change, without organisational change, will be largely in vain.

The meaning of culture

As a preliminary, let us return to the definition of culture as "the way we do things around here". There are several things to note about this formulation. First, culture is a characteristic of a group, be it as small as a

---

1 Andrew Hale makes some critical comments about this industry in his article, Foundations of Safety Science: A Postscript, *Safety Science* 2014, 67: 67.

family or as large as a nation. The phrase "around here", although vague, makes it clear that we are talking about the culture of some group, perhaps a work group, or perhaps a larger organisational group. The context would make this clearer.

Second, the practices are inherently collective — the way *we* do things. It is not just a question of the habits of individuals.

Third, and very importantly, there is a normative or psychological element to the expression. It carries with it the connotation that this is the right, or appropriate, or accepted way to do things. These judgements stem necessarily from shared assumptions, or values, or norms. What this means is that if someone fails to behave in the appropriate way, there will be consequences. These will not necessarily be severe — perhaps just a gentle reminder, or perhaps a prolonged, but meaningful silence. Whatever the case, the person concerned will be made aware that they have transgressed a group norm. In short, the emphasis on practices in this definition does not exclude the importance of norms and values. It is just a question of emphasis.

Academics have produced far more complex definitions but all their definitions accept that culture involves both behaviour and normative ideas, as described above. Logically, then, attempts to change culture can begin with behavior, or ideas. Hearts and minds approaches begin with ideas; behaviour-based safety begins, naturally enough, with behaviour.

Is one preferable? Theoretically, no, but in practice yes. If a company seeks to change a workplace culture, this can be done most easily by directing attention to practices because practices can be directly affected by management, while values and attitudes cannot. The organisational anthropologist Geert Hofstede puts the point admirably:

> Changing collective values of adult people in an intended direction is extremely difficult, if not impossible. Values do change, but not according to someone's master plan. Collective practices, however, depend on organisational characteristics like structures and systems, and can be influenced in more or less predictable ways by changing these.[2]

---

2   Quoted in Reason, J, *Managing the Risks of Organisational Accidents*, Aldershot, Ashgate, 1997, p 194.

An organisation which focuses its efforts on changing practices is not of course turning its back on value change. Psychology teaches us that human beings feel tension when their behaviour is out of alignment with their values.[3] There is consequently a tendency to bring the two into alignment. If the behaviour is effectively determined by the organisation, then the individual's values will tend to shift accordingly. Thus, if an organisation constrains an individual to behave safely, that individual will begin to value safe behaviour more highly in that context. To focus on practices therefore is a not a superficial strategy, which leaves what are perhaps more deep-seated aspects of a culture untouched. Changing practices will, in the end, change values and assumptions as well.

Think for example of attitudes to wearing seatbelts in cars. When seatbelts were first introduced, few people used them. Then they were made compulsory and non-compliers were fined. Accordingly, we changed our behaviour, if not our beliefs. But over time, beliefs themselves changed. Most people now believe it is a good idea to wear seatbelts.

Influencing hearts and minds

In light of the preceding discussion, the hearts and minds approach is handicapped from the outset because it is seeking to change values and ideas. Nevertheless, it is an extremely popular approach. Let us consider some examples. I shall deal with programs that have been implemented in two very well-known companies, as well as drawing on my own experience.

Shell's organisational maturity model

One of the most widely used and sophisticated examples of the hearts and minds approach was developed by a group of academics working with the petroleum company, Shell.[4] It was even called the "Hearts and Minds" program, which the company incorporated into a logo and managed to trademark, despite the fact that the expression itself long pre-dated its use by Shell.

The program had two aspects. First, it aimed to identify where an organisation stood on an organisational maturity ladder also known as a

---

3   Cognitive dissonance, see Kahn, A, *Social Psychology*, Dubuque, Brown, 1984, pp 115ff.

4   The following account is drawn from Hudson, P, Implementing a safety culture in a major multi-national, *Safety Science* 2007, 45: 697–722.

safety culture ladder. The five steps on the ladder are: pathological, reactive, calculative, proactive, generative (see Figure 3.1).

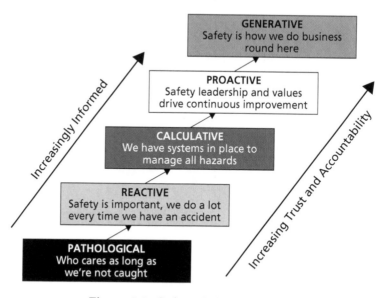

Figure 3.1: Safety Culture Ladder[5]

This ladder has been adapted by other consultancy firms and is one of the most common culture diagnostic tools in use in hazardous industries today.[6]

Diagnosis is one thing; moving companies up the ladder is quite another. Hence, the second aspect of the Shell program. It relied on developing or at least tapping into an "intrinsic motivation" for safety among its employees. In addition, there was to be "product marketing", the product being a higher level organisational culture. There were, coincidentally, five stages through which individual employees would need to pass: Ignorance, Awareness, Planning for Change, Acting Differently and Maintaining the Change. This was to be achieved by running workshops for up to 250,000 people, worldwide. To this end well over 100,000 brochures and several thousand

---

5   Hudson, op cit.

6   According to its creator, Patrick Hudson, "the culture ladder picture is nearly as well known as the Swiss Cheese picture". Given the ubiquity of the Swiss Cheese model in safety circles, this is quite a claim! See Hudson, P, Climbing the safety ladder, *OHS Professional* June 2017, p 17; see www.sia. org.au/sites/default/files/OHSJune2017.pdf, p 15.

extensive tool kits were distributed. This was a massive effort to change culture. Not surprisingly, the steps on the culture ladder, from pathological to generative, became part of the everyday vocabulary at Shell.

However, it is unclear how effective the program was at shifting the culture. Its designers intended the hearts and minds program to be evaluated a few years after it went live, but it never was.[7]

The principal designer, Patrick Hudson is very cautious in making claims about the effectiveness of this program. Some years after its implementation, he wrote a reflective and retrospective account of his experience. In it, he argued that to really embed such a change, what was necessary was "an organisational structure that rewards more advanced behaviours". For example, if the required behaviour was a willingness to challenge inappropriate written procedures, then the company would need to introduce KPIs that rewarded that behaviour, for example, number of times procedures are challenged. To guard against spurious challenges, this could be fine-tuned by counting only those cases in which the procedures were modified as a result of the challenge. This is a tacit admission that the goal of creating or tapping into an intrinsic motivation for safety had not been successful and that what was really needed was an extrinsic motivator. Here are Hudson's words:

> Setting up KPIs has shown that it is necessary to define an organisational structure to drive the entire process. Those at the top need to have a clearly expressed need to hear that action is taking place, even if what comes out of that action is personally embarrassing for those very top managers. What is essential for managers to create an advanced safety culture is an appetite for bad news, that the only really bad news is an unrestricted diet of good news.... An organisational structure that rewards more advanced behaviours is difficult for those who are still, essentially, reactive or early calculative, especially when there are no obvious and immediate benefits in terms of reduced incident rates, which is what they expect.[8]

In short, what Hudson is saying is that culture change requires a change in organisational structure and cannot be achieved by educational programs alone. One might go a step further and argue that if an appropriate system

---

7   Personal communication from Hudson.

8   Hudson, P, Implementing a safety culture in a major multi-national, *Safety Science* 2007, 45, p 717.

of rewards and recognition was in place, the required behaviour would be forthcoming, without the need for the elaborate program of workshops that Shell undertook. Unfortunately, according to Hudson, the Shell experience appears to be that the necessary organisational changes will be resisted by those at the top, who would rather that the hearts and minds of employees be won over without any fundamental change to the way the organisation does business.

BP's HRO program

These conclusions are reinforced by a culture change program run by BP at its Texas City Refinery, shortly before a major accident in 2005 that killed 15 people.[9] A number of Berkley-based social scientists developed a theory of "high reliability organisations" (HROs), organisations which have far fewer major incidents than might be expected. (HROs are the equivalent of generative organisations in the organisational maturity scale above.) In a nutshell, the theory was that HROs are especially sensitive to warning signs. Some relatively senior managers at BP were so taken with this theory that they invited these academics, turned consultants, to introduce an HRO educational program into BP's refinery operations. But the program made no difference at Texas City. In a survey a few months before the accident, respondents demonstrated that they had learnt the HRO language and were willing to talk about "weak signals" and "warning signs". However, in their view, BP itself was not taking warning signs seriously. Here are some comments from the survey:

- "We have warning signs occur every day; like pipe thinning." (A reference to corrosion)

- "Warning signs are everywhere, but the real ones ... [are] the lack of funding, and the application of band aids on top of band aids." (A reference to the shoddy maintenance work that was being done.)

- "The root cause of (a particular) fire was a lack of sufficient inquiry into weak signals."

Clearly these individuals had learnt the language, just as employees at Shell learnt the language of the organisational maturity ladder, but the organisation itself was unchanged. In particular, maintenance remained

---

9   Hopkins, A, *Failure to Learn: The Texas City Refinery disaster*, Sydney, CCH, 2008, Chapter 13.

woefully under-funded, and auditing and incident investigation remained demonstrably inadequate.

Educational programs have their place. But an educational program, by itself, cannot be expected to move the culture of an organisation in an HRO direction. What is needed is a different set of organisational practices in response to warning signs. This requires an organisational commitment that was lacking in BP at the time. The whole episode was a vivid demonstration of the limitations of attempting to change culture by changing mindset.

Enbridge

A third example concerns a program run by the pipeline company, Enbridge. This followed a major pipeline rupture and oil release in Michigan that cost the company more than $1b to clean up.[10] The enormous scale of the release was due to the failure of pipeline control room operators to recognise that the anomalous pressure results they were getting were due to pipeline rupture. They responded to these anomalies with classic psycho-social responses — normalising them, that is, finding alternative explanations and looking for signs that confirmed their erroneous interpretation — confirmation bias. The result was that they pumped oil out through the rupture for nearly two hours before they realised what was happening.

The psycho-social responses of the Enbridge operators were the very same responses displayed by operators confronted with anomalous test results in the lead-up to the blowout in the Gulf of Mexico. Enbridge was struck by this similarity and employed consultants to devise a training program to alert employees to the dangers of these ways of thinking, if you like, to change their hearts and minds. All this was very well intentioned. But by itself it would almost certainly have failed. These psychological responses are all too human, and trying to change them amounts to trying to change human nature. Enbridge was aware of this problem and explained its position as follows:

> Human factors reflect the way our brains are wired and how we understand the world around us. . . . . But when we're aware of human factors we can reduce their impact, making safe decisions even in the face of competing pressures.

---

10   Hayes, J and Hopkins, A, *Nightmare Pipeline Failures*, Sydney, CCH, 2014.

Unfortunately, however, helping people to understand why they make mistakes doesn't necessarily help them to avoid making those mistakes. That requires a different approach. What Enbridge needed to do was devise much clearer procedures and much tighter supervision and auditing to ensure compliance.[11]

Fortunately, that is exactly what it did. The company subsequently redesigned its organisational structure to give greater prominence to the management of major hazards. This will be dealt with in Chapter 5.

Research evidence on the limitations of hearts and minds campaigns

The preceding comments are to some extent anecdotal. There is, however, a good deal of research evidence calling into question the value of hearts and minds campaigns more generally. From time to time, there are mass media campaigns to change people's health-and-safety-related behavior, focused on matters such as smoking, drinking, diet, exercise, drug taking and seatbelt wearing. An exhaustive review of the evidence of the effectiveness of these campaigns produced some important conclusions.[12] First, it was difficult to gauge the effects of these media campaigns because they were often accompanied by other policy changes designed to encourage the desired behaviour. For example, media campaigns to encourage seatbelt wearing in the US have usually been accompanied by tougher enforcement of seatbelt wearing laws, something which the campaigns themselves have highlighted. "Click It or Ticket" was the slogan of one such campaign. These campaigns have had some success, but it is very likely that this was a result of the enforcement activity, rather than the media campaigns themselves. This is clearly illustrated by campaigns about alcohol consumption. Media campaigns to reduce drink driving have met with some success because they are associated with enforcement activity, while campaigns to reduce alcohol intake more generally have been largely unsuccessful. Furthermore, research evidence shows that even where short-term changes in behaviour can be attributed to a media campaigns, "sustained effects are difficult to maintain after campaigns end". Finally, and most importantly, mass media

---

11   For more details, see Hayes and Hopkins, op cit, pp 44–48.

12   Wakefield, A, Loken, B and Homlik, R, Use of mass media campaigns to change health behaviour, *Lancet* 2010 Oct 9: 1261–71.

Chapter 25

Ryck got up early, showered and shaved. He wanted to catch Colonel Ketter earlier in his working day, when the colonel might be in a better mood. He leaned over and kissed his still-sleeping wife on the forehead, then slipped out of the room and house and into the Hyundai.

It was a short drive to base, and his mind was racing as he considered his options. Now that it was morning, he wondered if he'd made the right choice.

The gate AI cleared him, and he drove to battalion, skipping his company CP. This early, there was only the watch officer and his duty staff up and about.

"You're up early, Captain Lysander," Lt Parsons, from Bravo company, said as Ryck entered the building.

"Need to use the comms," Ryck told him.

"Sergeant Smith, why don't you open the comms shed for the captain," Parsons told his duty NCO.

Sgt Smith pulled out the access badges and led Ryck down the passage to comms. He had to look through the badges to find the right one. He held it up to the access port, and the hatch swung open.

"Stop by the duty office, sir, when you're done so I can lock up, please," the sergeant said as he left Ryck to his call.

Ryck logged in, then punched in Col Ketter's office. Within moments, the same woman as before came on the screen. Ryck thought he saw a small look of displeasure cross her face, but she told him she would connect him to the colonel.

A few moments later, the screen switched to the colonel.

"Captain Lysander, I trust you have made your decision?" Colonel Ketter asked.

Unlike with his secretary, the look of distaste on his face was more pronounced. Ryck couldn't blame him. Threatening to go over an officer's head was sure to raise more than a little anger.

"Yes, sir, I wanted to say a few things."

When Ryck paused, the colonel prompted him, "So say it. I've got a lot on my table today."

How am I going to say it?

Ryck took a deep breath, then jumped right in. "Sir, about yesterday, I abjectly apologize for my actions and words."

The colonel was visibly surprised. This obviously was not what he'd expected.

teasing. Noah was better in his own world, but Esther craved attention, craved love.

It was Ryck's job to raise his kids, to bring them up right. It was a daunting task, and one he wasn't sure he could handle. Hannah was better than him at this. All he could do was try his utmost to be the best father he could be.

Looking at her, he made up his mind. He knew what he had to do.

telling the child about their lives, how they got their food, how the environment was important to them.

"Oh, thank you, Daddy," she said, lost in the block.

Ryck had gotten both presents at the PX earlier in the day. Neither twin was old enough to appreciate something specifically from one of the planets he'd been on, not that there had been anything unique enough to buy anyway. No, a PX gift was good enough.

"Give me five minutes, Ryck, and dinner will be on the table, Hannah told him.

He gave her an air kiss and sat down on the couch, watching his two children play. Noah hadn't altered his tempo, but he seemed happy enough to be simply making noise. Esther was quiet with only a few "ohs" and "look at that" exclaimed as he watched her.

He missed this. The kids were so much bigger than when he'd left, and he resented losing out on their growth and development. But he'd chosen his path, and this was just one price he had to pay. He thought back to Col Ketter's statement, that he could just resign his commission. If he did that, he could be with his family every night. He could be part of them instead of just a transient observer who bounced in and out of their lives.

As if reading his thoughts, as if she could tell Ryck was troubled, Esther looked up at him, a look of concern on her face. She placed the Animal Friend on the table and crept up on the couch. Ryck kept his arm down on his side and she slowly moved in, her little body pressed up against his. She wormed her head between his arm and his body, then slowly forced her way up and under his arm. Her little arm reached up and encircled his waist.

His snugglebunny. She'd been doing this since she could crawl, and it had become something between them, a bond between father and daughter. Now that she had gained her position, Ryck relaxed his arm, putting it around her and pulling her tight.

He looked down at her, filled with love. It was hard to believe that Hannah and he had created such two perfect little people.

What would she think of her father, he wondered, as she got into her teen years? Would she resent his absences? Accepting the orders would mean three whole years away from his family. Would she resent that he was not always there for her? If he pulled strings to get the order changed, would she resent it when the other kids told her that her father was an asshole, that their fathers hated him?

Most of the time, she seemed stronger than her brother, but Ryck thought she would be more bothered than him by other kids'

"I missed you too, Daddy! Mommy and Noah missed you too," she said in his ear, her little arms wrapped around his neck.

Ryck looked over her shoulder to where Noah stood, taking Hannah's hand that Esther had dropped in his. He looked up at Ryck uncertainly.

Ryck felt a twinge of guilt. Noah was a loving boy, but not as outgoing as his sister. Ryck being gone so much had an effect on him, and not a good one.

"Aren't you going to hug your father?" Ryck asked.

Noah looked up at Hannah, who nodded and urged him forward. Noah dutifully walked up to Ryck and hugged his leg. Ryck squatted, shifting Esther to one arm and enveloping his son with his other.

"Welcome home, Captain Lysander," Charise said from the door.

"Charise, I keep telling you its Ryck," he told her.

"I know," she said. "I just, well, I'll leave you to your homecoming. I've got Abby in the hover, and Brian'll be home soon."

Abby was Charise's own baby and Brian her husband.

"OK, Charise, thanks. I'll call you later," Hannah said as she left.

Charise was right, though. This was the real homecoming. The twins had been asleep when he'd gotten home the night before, and while he'd hugged them both in their beds, and they had mumbled greetings of a sort, they were too far gone to remember much. In the morning, and waking up early, he'd gone to work before they woke up.

"Hey, I brought you two something," Ryck said, perking both of them up. He let go of them and opened the entrance closet, taking out two wrapped presents. He handed them to the twins, who squealed as they tore off the paper wrapping.

"Oh, top special," Noah said as he pulled the Miyama organ out of the box. This was the child's version with four different instruments. They music could be created by hitting each protruding key, or recorded songs could be played. He immediately hit the image of the drum and started pounding away.

"Oh, thanks," Hannah said with mock concern, rolling her eyes.

Esther took a few more moments, not wanting to tear the wrapping paper. She took out the vision block and peered in. This was the Animal Friend block, and inside were holos of various animals. The images were real, but the animals spoke to the child, campaigns can be effectively defeated by lack of supporting policies and products, contrary advertising and contradictory social norms.

It follows from all of this that, in an organisational context, hearts and minds campaigns, by themselves, cannot be expected to have a significant sustained effect on behaviour.

Culture as a virus

There is one particular hearts and minds approach I mention here because more than any other, it is the absolute antithesis of the structural thesis that motivates this book. This is the idea of culture as virus. In this view, culture spreads from person to person just like a biological virus. According to its influential proponent, Leandro Herrero, "there are great similarities between biological infection and idea infection". Furthermore, the assumption is that peer influence is greater than hierarchical influence. This is elaborated in the following passage:

> Granted, some of these journeys may require changes in structures and processes. But the ultimate real change is behavioural. These and other cultural transformations are shaped by the behaviours of individuals and small groups, not by a top-down, push from management. Change and mobilisation of people are pull effects, a social contagion, a social movement, with the leadership engine in the grass roots and back-stage support from the Executive floor, not the other way around.[13]

The first sentence is a major qualification to the whole argument, almost a repudiation of it, one might think. But leaving that sentence aside, this is an extraordinary conception of how change occurs in a large organisation. It will seem quite unrealistic to anyone who has worked in a bureaucratic environment, especially one that has an "executive floor". Moreover, it is a conception that has very little academic support, as I discuss below. Herrero's notions of change are arguably more applicable to the way social movements operate, but to transpose them into an organisational context is just wishful thinking.

---

13   www.viralchange.com/.

Leaders create cultures

The structural perspective that I am adopting in this book can be contrasted with another important approach to understanding the source of culture change — leadership. Organisational psychologist Edgar Schein puts the point as follows:

"Leaders create and change cultures, while managers and administrators live within them."[14]

This is a deliberately provocative statement designed to flatter top leaders into action, but his point is clear enough. If the culture of an organisation is secretive, it is because its leadership has encouraged secretive behaviour; if it is bureaucratic, it is because its leaders have encouraged bureaucratic functioning.

To what extent is this in conflict with the structuralist account? In the hands of some culture change consultants it is flatly contradictory. Take DuPont, which regards itself as having an exemplary approach to safety.[15] The DuPont consulting firm advocates *felt leadership* as a means of promoting a safety culture. Among the principles of felt leadership are the following:

- Be visible to the organisation.

- Be relentless about time with people.

- Recognise your role as teacher/trainer.

- Develop your own safety functioning skills and pass them along to the organisation.

- Behave and lead as you desire others to do.

- Confirm and reconfirm safety as the #1 value.

- Place continuous emphasis and clarity around safety expectations.

- Show a passion for ZERO injuries, illnesses, and incidents.[16]

---

14   Schein, E, *Organisational Culture and Leadership 2nd ed*, San Francisco, Jossey-Bass, 1992, p 5.

15   DuPont's reputation was seriously undermined when an explosion at its LaPorte plant in Texas killed four men. www.texastribune.org/2015/07/09/new-osha-penalties-dupont-after-deadly-la-porte-le/.

16   www.rimbach.com/scripts/Article/IHN/Number.idc?Number=113, accessed 24/4/2018.

This is a highly individualised understanding of the role of leadership in creating cultures of safety. There is no reference at all to organisational structure.

If we return to Schein, the organisational psychologist, we get a rather different answer to the question of how leaders create cultures:

> [Leaders create cultures by] what they systematically pay attention to. This can mean anything from what they notice and comment on to what they measure, control, reward and in other ways systematically deal with.

It is immediately apparent from this comment that identifying leaders as the source of culture is not inconsistent with the structural perspective. The point is that if something is important to top leaders, they will set in place the structures that are necessary to ensure the outcomes they want. They will institute the necessary measurement and reporting systems, the necessary systems of control and the appropriate systems of reward. In other words, leaders create the structures that will in turn institutionalise the kind of organisational culture they want.

On-time running in the rail system, discussed in Chapter 2, is an excellent example of this process. Rail industry leaders value on-time running above almost everything else because they are under enormous public and political pressure to ensure that trains run on time. So they employ a substantial apparatus of signallers, controllers and inspectors to achieve this end, and they examine the on-time running figures twice a day, so that performance during morning and evening peaks can be separately assessed.[17] To repeat, leaders create the structures that in turn create the cultures they want.

Finally, we can turn this around and say that if the organisational structures have resulted in a defective safety culture, it is because the leaders are not sufficiently motivated to create the structures that will yield the culture they purportedly want. After a major accident they often are, as we shall see in later chapters.

---

17 See Hopkins, A, Railway culture and safety: The Glenbrook train crash. In *Safety Culture and Risk: The Organisational Causes of Disasters*, Sydney, CCH, 2005.

Behaviour-Based Safety (BBS)

We turn now to a strategy that focuses on changing behaviours, rather than ideas or values — behaviour-based safety (BBS). There is often dispute about exactly what BBS is, so to be clear, I quote from one of its leading exponents, Dominic Cooper:

> Behavioral Safety [or BBS] attempts to identify those unsafe behaviors implicated in the majority of injuries. These behaviors and/or their proxies (e.g., hoses left lying across walkways) are developed into specific behavioral checklists. Trained observers use these to monitor and record people's work behavior on a regular basis (e.g., daily). Derived from the observation results, 'Percent safe' scores provide feedback, so people can track their progress against self-set, assigned or participative improvement goals. Feedback mechanisms include verbal feedback at the point of observation, graphical charts and/or written performance summaries so corrective actions can be taken. Results indicate significant reductions in injury rates are possible within a relatively short time with the impact lasting for many years.[18]

This is sometimes seen as a narrow approach, in contrast to a broader cultural approach.[19] In one sense it is, in that it sets out to influence behaviour directly, rather than by first changing ideas and expecting this to change behaviour. On the other hand, as noted earlier, if we change behaviour, values and attitudes tend to align over time to the point where the new way becomes "the way we do things around here". In other words, the outcome may well be culture change. If, as Cooper says, the impact lasts for many years, that is clearly what has happened. From this point of view, BBS can be viewed as an attempt to change culture.

However, BBS has traditionally focused on personal safety as opposed to process safety or major hazard risk. Moreover, as is clear from the preceding description it relies on observing and counting discrete, frequently occurring events. This is fine for frequently occurring events such as rolling, or not rolling hoses, and holding, or not holding hand rails. But the events that precede major accidents are not of this kind. They are often decisions rather

---

18   Cooper, D, Safety leadership: application in construction site, *G Ital Med Lav Erg* 2010; 32:1, Suppl A, Psicol, p A18.

19   Sharman, A, *From Accidents to Zero*, London, Routledge, 2016, pp 17–18.

than actions, and they may concern relatively unusual events such as occur at startup or shutdown. These kinds of events are far less susceptible to the processes of counting and feedback envisaged by behavior-based safety. BBS is therefore not a strategy that can be readily adapted to changing the cultures (the ways we do things around here) that are implicated in major accidents.[20]

Conclusion

Changing organisational structures is not the preferred approach of the culture change industry. Culture change consultants adopt the far more individualist approach of winning the hearts and minds and/or changing individual behaviour, approaches which leave basic organisational structures unchanged. As a result, the hoped-for culture change remains elusive.

None of the approaches discussed above undermine the argument of this book. In fact, as I have shown, some of them provide implicit support. Interestingly, organisations that have suffered major accidents seldom embark of campaigns to change the mindset of their employees, nor do they turn to behaviour-based safety. They make organisational changes which are designed to manage major hazard risk more effectively. We shall see examples of this in later chapters.

---

20 For a more biting critique see Dekker www.safetydifferently.com/the-original-hearts-and-minds-campaign-and-the-dereliction-of-behavior-based-safety/.

Chapter 4
The anarchist school

In my consultancy work in hazardous organisations, I have encountered some senior managers talking quite excitedly about a further approach that potentially challenges the structure argument. It is associated with the names of two high-profile writers, Sidney Dekker and Eric Hollnagel, who constitute what might be called the anarchist school of safety.[1] In this view, safety is best achieved by abolishing centrally imposed rules and procedures and relying on the intrinsic motivation of people exposed to hazards to develop their own rules of safe behaviour. This has great intuitive appeal because it is based on the idea of humans as autonomous, creative beings, rather than mindless rule followers. We must ask, however: just how relevant are the ideas of the anarchist school to the management of major hazard risk? Interestingly, neither Dekker nor Hollnagel claim that they are. The idea that safety anarchism might be an appropriate way to deal with major hazard risk therefore involves a serious misunderstanding of what these writers intend, and if implemented, it could be dangerously counterproductive. The aim of this short chapter is to outline briefly the anarchist perspective and to demonstrate that it does not offer an alternative to the arguments of this book, and nor is it intended to.

Dekker and Safety Differently

Dekker outlines his views in two books, *Safety Differently* and *The Safety Anarchist*. He has also released a video on the subject — "Safety Differently: the Movie" — which he narrates. His first words in the video are arresting:

> Imagine a space, a space in which there are no rules, a space in which people themselves can determine the best course of action, a space in which people spontaneously negotiate, and collaborate in order to create the safest outcomes, for everyone. In this space a new type

---

1   Dekker, S, *The Safety Anarchist*, Routledge, 2017.

of humanity emerges. No one is telling them. They figure it out on the spot.[2]

This is indeed a radical and disruptive vision. Perhaps Dekker is simply taking poetic licence at the beginning of his movie. But no. His vision is based on a traffic experiment that was carried out in Holland in the early 2000s in the town of Drachten. The main roads intersection in the town routinely experienced gridlock, as well as a significant number of serious accidents each year. The Dutch traffic engineer, Hans Monderman, believed that the regulation of traffic, using lines on roads, signs and traffic lights was contributing to this problem, rather than helping. He believed that traffic controls of this nature encouraged people to switch off mentally and to assume that just by following the rules they would be safe. So he proposed that lights and lines be done away with at the intersection. This would require pedestrians, bicyclists and motorists approaching the intersection to be far more alert and cautious. His proposal was implemented, and indeed people behaved far more respectfully and carefully than previously — catching each other's eye before entering the intersection, so as to coordinate their movements. Low and behold, gridlock disappeared, and over the next two years there were far fewer accidents.

Monderman's ideas were part of a broader movement to design public space in urban areas as *shared space*, with all those moving through the space having a joint responsibility for safety. These ideas have been successfully implemented in urban areas in several countries.

Dekker has taken this principle and applied it to a different domain — workplace health and safety. He reasons that if workers have to negotiate and collaborate to ensure their own safety, their intrinsic motivation to behave safely will come into play and the workplace will be safer than it currently is.

He was given the opportunity to implement these ideas by the Woolworths chain of supermarkets and set up a controlled experiment using 30 of the company's retail food stores. The results were generally supportive of his ideas.[3]

---

2   www.safetydifferently.com/safety-differently-the-movie/
3   For more details, see Dekker, S, *The Safety Anarchist*, London, Routledge, 2018, pp 178–185.

But how generalisable is this approach? Does it apply to highway safety, or flight safety, or the safety of buildings from the point of view of occupants? Most importantly in the present context, does it apply to process safety or, more generally, major hazard risk? Dekker himself raises this question.[4] He concludes that his proposals are more relevant in some contexts than in others. In relation to flight safety, for instance, he has this to say:

> I have been flying the Boeing 737 for a while as a co-pilot. I learnt very quickly that it makes no sense to vary the sequence of actions to start up the jet. Varying the order, or timing, or even substance of some of the actions would confuse the other pilot tremendously; it could result in a hung start, or an over-heated engine, a fire, or any other risk problem. So you learn the rules, you apply the rules, you don't deviate.[5]

So how about process safety? Can the Drachten experience be generalised to this context? One way to answer this question is to identify the features of the Drachten shared space and consider to what extent they apply in the process safety context. I have identified the following nine characteristics:

- There is a *shared space* with clearly defined participants.

- The risk is managed entirely by people in the shared space. No one outside the space has any role in managing the immediate risk.

- Risk management is interpersonal. Negotiating the space successfully requires eye contact and an implicit negotiation about who goes first. It involves a measure of trust, on a one-to-one basis.

- The danger is shared. Everyone in the space is in danger of one form or another. For the pedestrian and the cyclist, the consequences are potentially fatal. For the motorist who injures or kills a pedestrian or cyclist, there are legal consequences[6], and if one motorist collides with another, the potential consequence is at least damage to one's vehicle. Everyone in the shared space has a very personal interest in avoiding these consequences.

---

4   Op cit, pp 177–8.

5   Op cit, pp 20.

6   Under Dutch law, If the cyclist is an adult, the motorist is absolutely liable for at least 50% of the damages/injuries with the remaining 50% shared depending on the degree of fault. See www.blogs.crikey.com.au/theurbanist/2013/06/13/are-dutch-motorists-strictly-liable-if-they-collide-with-a-cyclist/.

- The danger is immediate. On entering the space the danger is right now, not at some indeterminate time in the future. One false move right now could lead to a collision, or worse, a fatality.

- The danger is temporary. A person moving into the shared space will soon be out of it. The high level of concentration required to manage the risk is only for this brief and predictable period of time.

- The required behaviour is vital to collision avoidance, not just precautionary, reducing the likelihood of collision. Without that increased pressure on the brake, or movement of the steering wheel or handle bars, the collision will almost certainly occur. There is a direct causal connection between the required safe behaviour and the safe outcome.

- The risk is well understood by everyone, and people in the space are generally competent to manage the risk.

- The people in the space are operating autonomously, not as part of a larger organisation that may be systematically influencing the behavior in question.

Few, if any, of these features are true for major hazard risks. For a start, there is no meaningful *shared space* in which major hazards are both confronted and managed. Decisions about the management of major hazards are often taken by people not immediately exposed to them. I shall not go through the preceding list in detail, but I invite interested readers to carry out this exercise for themselves. If you do, you will see that the Drachten experience is utterly inapplicable for major hazard risk. "Safety anarchism", therefore, offers no alternative to the structuralist approach advocated in this book. Those who seek to generalise it to this context should be very careful indeed.

Hollnagel and Safety-II

Eric Hollnagel is a Danish safety scientist well known for his distinction between Safety-I and Safety-II. Safety-I is the "old" way of doing things, he says. It relies on complex safety management systems which require workers to follow rules and procedures. Inevitably, the rules and procedures are imperfect, and following them can lead to perverse and sometime even dangerous outcomes. On the other hand, in the Safety-II approach, it is the creativity and expertise of front line workers that keep them safe, not slavish adherence to safety rules. The job of safety professionals is therefore to learn from workers, and to encourage their creativity.

According to Hollnagel, Safety-I focuses on why things go wrong, and in particular, why humans make errors. From this point of view, humans are the problem. Safety-II focuses on why things go right, which is nearly all the time, and it seeks to learn from this. From this point of view, the human capacity to innovate is part of the solution.

Hollnagel further contrasts these two perspectives as follows. Safety-I sees the variability of human performance as a source of accidents; while Safety-II sees it as the source of what goes right, as well. Here's why. Systems and procedures are always imperfect, requiring some adaptive input from the worker.

> [So] when such systems perform reliably, it is because people are flexible and adaptive, rather than because the systems are perfectly thought out and designed. Humans are therefore no longer a liability and performance variability is not a threat. On the contrary, the variability of everyday performance is necessary for the system to function, and is the source of successes as well as of failures. Because successes and failures both depend on performance variability, failures cannot be prevented by eliminating it. In other words, *safety cannot be managed by imposing constraints on normal work.*[7]

The last sentence sounds like a complete rejection of Safety-I. But in fact Hollnagel does not mean to reject Safety-I. Instead, he says,

> It is important to emphasise that Safety-I and Safety-II represent two complementary views of safety rather than two incompatible or conflicting approaches. Many of the existing practices can therefore continue to be used, although possibly with a different emphasis. But the transition to a Safety-II view will also include some new types of practice.[8]

So in the end, Safety-II does not involve the wholesale abandonment of rules. Rather it involves drawing to a greater extent on the expertise of the front line, for example, in the *formulation* of rules, to ensure that they are

---

7 Hollnagel, E, and Leonhardt, J, *From Safety-I to Safety-II: A White Paper*, Eurocontrol, 2013, P15. Emphasis added.

8 Op cit, pp 22.

fit for purpose. Hollnagel's proposals are therefore not as inconsistent with the conventional approach as they appear at first sight.

The importance of procedures for managing major hazards

The preceding comments raise the question: why are procedures so important, particularly in hazardous industries? Jim Reason provides a succinct answer.

> Procedures communicate task-know-how.... Collectively they comprise the accumulated craft wisdom and practical knowledge of the company as a whole. Good procedures should tell people the most efficient and safest way of carrying out particular tasks.... Good procedures are necessary for three reasons:
>
> 1. Many jobs are too complicated for their individual steps to be self-evident.
>
> 2. The information necessary to perform tasks correctly is usually too much to be carried reliably in human memory.
>
> 3. People change faster than jobs. This means that the organization needs a means of passing on standardized task information from one person to the next.[9]

Reason refers above to "good" procedures. Of course, procedures and standards can be clumsy, inadequate and confusing. There are two ways of responding to this. The first is to put resources into improving them. This will include getting input from those who have to apply them to ensure that they take account of the particular circumstances of users and are practical to follow. The second way to deal with the problem is to abandon centrally imposed procedures and standards and leave it to the good sense of the those exposed to the hazards. This is the anarchist solution, which is no solution at all for major hazard risk.

This is not the place for a comprehensive discussion of the ideas of Hollnagel and Dekker, which have merit in the right context. The point is simply that they are largely irrelevant to the management of major hazards.

---

9   Reason, J, *Organizational Accidents Revisited*, Ashgate, Farnham, 2016.

Companies should be very cautious about trying to apply anarchist ideas in this context. Major hazards need to be managed centrally and companies need to be organisationally structured to ensure that this is done effectively.

Mindless versus Mindful compliance

While safety anarchism is not a strategy that can be readily applied in the major hazard context, it does embody some important insights. In particular, the attempt to achieve safe operation by means of procedures and procedural compliance can degenerate into mindless almost ritualistic behaviour, where the goal is no longer safe operation, but simply compliance with procedures. This mindset can sometimes lead to dangerous outcomes. The Gulf of Mexico oil well blowout provides an instructive example.[10] The engineers responsible for drilling operations were constrained by various regulatory requirements. At certain points they asked the regulator to exempt them from the normal requirements, to make the job easier. Such exemptions were readily granted by the regulator, which was seriously under-resourced and had no real appreciation of the significance of the exemptions being granted. Unfortunately, these exemptions increased the risk of blowout. It is apparent that the goal of the engineers was to ensure that they had this regulatory approval for what they wanted to do, not to ensure that it was safe. For this reason, I use the term *mindless* compliance — compliance without regard to the safety consequences. Mindless compliance, then, was one of the contributing factors to the Gulf of Mexico accident.

The US nuclear submarine fleet has wrestled with this issue and provides a good example of what can be called *mindful* compliance.[11] The culture of the fleet requires a very high level of procedural compliance. But there is no assumption that the procedure writers have covered every conceivable situation. On the contrary, the assumption is that from time to time situations will arise that are not covered by procedures and where unthinking compliance could lead to undesirable outcomes. Crews are trained to be alert to this, and when such situations arise, to stop the job and raise the issue with their superiors. Notice that the crew cannot simply

---

10   See Hopkins, *Disastrous Decisions*, op cit, pp 143–4.

11   DiGeronimo, M and Koonce, B, *Extreme Operational Excellence: Applying the US Nuclear Submarine Culture to your Organization*, Colorado, Outskirts Press, 2016. See also Bieder, C and Bourrier, M (eds), *Trapping Safety into Rules*, Farnham, Ashgate, 2013.

develop their own solutions; it must be done in consultation with superiors. In this way proposed deviations can be carefully scrutinised and justified.

Mindful compliance is an idea that solves the problem that safety anarchists identify, but for which, they have no real solution in the case of major hazard risks. It legitimates a high level of procedural compliance which is nevertheless conditional on whether this compliance is meeting the overarching goal of safety. It is a solution that requires "keeping the mind engaged", so as to be able to recognise when procedures may be inadequate, and it requires speaking up about these inadequacies. Encouraging mindful compliance honours the intelligence of workers and promotes initiative, rather than stifling it. These ideas will be developed further in Chapter 11.

Chapter 5

BP's structural transformation: from decentralised to centralised

BP's near-death experience in its Gulf of Mexico blowout in 2010 provides a vivid case study of the relationship between organisational structure and safety. The blowout killed 11 men and did tens of billions of dollars of environmental damage. Within weeks BP shares had lost half their value. Over the next six months they had recovered half this loss but for years afterwards the share price remained 25% lower than it had been before the disaster.[1] BP was forced to sell off numerous assets to pay its bills. The accident would have destroyed a smaller company, but somehow, BP survived.

I have already written a book length account of the disaster, *Disastrous Decisions*. In this chapter I want to focus on what was arguably the most important contributing factor, BP's organisational structure. BP also regarded this as a critical factor, requiring a complete redesign of the company, which allows us to conduct an illuminating before-and-after comparison.

This chapter will be the most detailed case study in the book. Most of the organisational theory used in the book is introduced here in order to make sense of the BP story. This theory will also be drawn on in some other cases discussed in the book. I treat theory in this subordinate way quite deliberately. It is an aid to understanding the world around us, not an end itself. It is introduced only as necessary, to help make sense of, in this case, the world of hazardous organisations. The next two sections below will introduce the theoretical ideas necessary to understand BP's transformation. After that, the BP case will be described in detail.

---

1   See Hopkins, A and Maslen, S *Risky rewards: How Company Bonuses Affect Safety*, Ashgate, Farnham, 2015, pp 36–7.

Centralised and decentralised structures

Large corporations, such as international oil companies, must choose between decentralised and more centralised modes of operation. In the decentralised mode, the corporation consists of a number of largely autonomous business units, with a small corporate centre, whose role is essentially one of financial management of its portfolio of businesses. At the other end of the spectrum is the centralised corporation in which many "functions" are managed centrally, leaving far less decision-making to the local assets or businesses. When discussing organisational structure, the term "function" refers to hierarchies of specialised employees, for example an engineering function and a human resource function.

The decentralised mode provides individual business units with more scope to innovate, both technically and in terms of markets, and is theoretically more profitable. However, this can be at the expense of the technical rigor which is required when dealing with catastrophic risk.

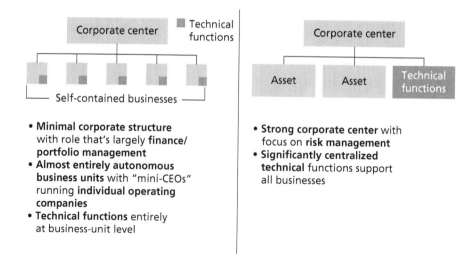

Figure 5.1: Decentralised versus centralised organisational structures

The consulting firm McKinsey[2] portrays the situation in Figure 5.1. In the decentralised structure on the left, the technical functions in each

---

2   Handscomb, C et al, The oil and gas organisation of the future, McKinsey, September 2016.

constituent business are subordinated to the needs of the business unit and may be compromised in the process. In the centralised structure on the right, the technical functions are answerable to the centre and not to the assets, to which they provide services. They are, therefore, less likely to bend to the will of the asset managers. This makes for a safer but also less flexible system.

Companies sometimes cycle between these two models in a manner that suggests that they are simply following the latest fashion. But there is a clear rationale for choosing between these models. Where operations face catastrophic risks, the centralised approach is desirable. For lower risk assets, a decentralised model may be preferable. Here is how McKinsey puts it in the context of the oil and gas industry:

> Managing risk — technical, commercial and operational — is ... a compelling reason to centralise and is particularly evident for high-complexity plays [groups of oil fields] such as deepwater, frontier and liquefied natural gas (LNG) assets.
>
> In parallel, the rise of lower-risk asset types such as light, tight oil [eg shale oil] has changed thinking about the role of the corporate centre. In particular, success in unconventional and late-life operations [that is, low pressure and therefore less risky operations] requires local coordination and integrated decision-making at the front line — not layers of review from corporate.[3]

This discussion offers a top-down view. For a fuller understanding of the distinction, we need also to view the situation from the bottom-up. In the present context, it will be useful to think about just one technical function — engineering — and to consider how individual engineers relate to line managers in a business unit or asset.

There are two possible reporting lines for an engineer working at a particular site. They may report directly to the manager who is accountable for the site's business performance, or they may report to a more senior engineer who is not responsible to management at that site. This more senior engineer may report to a business unit one level up, or to a more senior engineer, and so on. This ancillary engineering line must report at

---

3   Handscomb et al 2016.

some point to a person accountable for business performance, the ultimate possibility being that the engineering line goes all the way to the CEO. These possibilities are presented, in a simplified form, in Figure 5.2. The solid lines are lines of formal accountability, while dotted lines refer to the provision of engineering services to line managers. These terms are discussed further below.

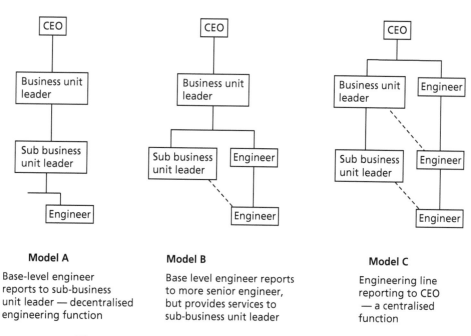

Model A	**Model B**	**Model C**
Base-level engineer reports to sub-business unit leader — decentralised engineering function	Base level engineer reports to more senior engineer, but provides services to sub-business unit leader	Engineering line reporting to CEO — a centralised function

Figure 5.2: Three models for an engineering function

These different models have different consequences for decision making. Consider a situation where a base-level engineer is proposing the best engineering practice, while the site manager (sub-business unit leader) is willing to settle for something less than best, but arguably still adequate, in order to reduce cost. In model A, the ultimate decision maker is the site manager (sub-business unit leader) and the engineering arguments may end up being discounted too readily. However, in model B, the base-level engineer is answerable to a more senior engineer, who is in a position to elevate the decision to the business unit leader, one level up. Model C enables further elevation, to the CEO in this simple example. Evidently, the longer the engineering line of accountability, the greater the likelihood that best practice engineering solutions will be adopted.

There is another important difference. Where the base-level engineer reports formally to a site manager, their performance agreement with that manager is likely to emphasise contribution to the commercial goals of the site, perhaps at the expense of engineering excellence. Over time, the judgement of the base-level engineer is likely to be compromised. On the other hand, where the base-level engineer reports to a more senior engineer, the performance agreement is more likely to emphasise engineering goals.

Finally, the longer the engineering line of accountability the better is the career structure for engineers within the organisation, and the greater the chances of mentoring and continued training for engineers.

Where differences of opinion are resolved at the base asset level, without involving higher level decision makers, we can speak of decentralised decision making; where the organisational structure encourages differences to be raised at a higher level, as in models B and C, we can speak of centralised decision making. While the language of centralisation/decentralisation suggests just two options, this discussion makes it clear that there are degrees of centralisation, and that organisations may position themselves at various points along the spectrum.

Box 5.1: Solid and dotted lines

It is difficult to find any clear discussion of the distinction between solid and dotted lines, even though these terms are widely used in large organisations. This box attempts to fill the gap.

In most large organisations, each employee has a supervisor to whom they are accountable. This generally means that the supervisor will conduct an annual performance review which directly affects the person's pay and promotion prospects. The supervisor will therefore be the most influential person in the employee's immediate environment. This is represented by a solid line on the organisational chart.

The meaning of a dotted line is not so clear cut. In fact, it varies, and there are at least two distinct possibilities (A and B in Figure 5.3).

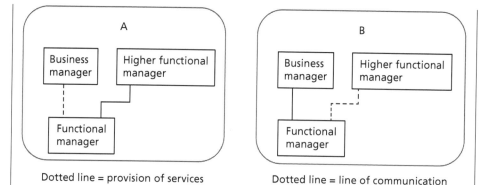

Dotted line = provision of services   Dotted line = line of communication

Figure 5.3: Possible reporting arrangements

In both models in this diagram, the lower level functional managers are positioned to the left, to represent the fact that they are co-located with the business unit.[4] Consider, first, possibility A. The dotted line represents the *provision of services* to the business line by the subordinate functional manager on site. For example, if the function is engineering, or health, safety & environment (HSE), then the dotted line represents the provision of engineering or HSE services, supervised closely by a higher level functional manager (via a solid line). For possibility B, however, the functional manager located on site is providing services via a solid line to the business manager, to whom they are formally accountable. The dotted line in this situation must therefore represent something else. Some organisations describe it as a *line of communication*,[5] a rather vague notion that encompasses a multitude of possibilities. In some such cases, higher functional managers may exercise considerable influence over lower level functional mangers via the dotted line; in other cases, their influence may be negligible.

BP's organisational structure before Macondo

The Gulf of Mexico blowout is widely referred to as the Deepwater Horizon disaster, based on the name of the drilling rig involved. At the time, BP

---

4   This is not a convention I have been able to follow consistently in this book.

5   After its Texas City Refinery accident, BP introduced dotted lines between engineers in various parts of the organisation which it described as "engineers talking to each other". See Hopkins, A, *Failure to Learn: The BP Texas City Refinery disaster*, Sydney, CCH, 2008, p 102.

was drilling a well named Macondo. For this reason, the accident is also referred to as the Macondo disaster. I shall try to refer to it consistently as the Gulf of Mexico accident although at times Macondo will be a more convenient term.

At the time of the Gulf of Mexico accident, BP was among the most decentralised of the major oil and gas companies. It consisted of a series of relatively autonomous business units, loosely tied together at the corporate centre in London.

This structure had not changed much since the disastrous accident at BP's Texas City refinery five years earlier.[6] Two formal inquiries at the time of that accident identified BP's decentralised organisational structure as a contributing factor.[7] In particular, the Baker report noted that in BP's decentralised organisational framework:

> the refinery plant manager has a tremendous amount of discretion in running the business. Some people at BP refer to this an "empowerment ethos". As [CEO] Browne has described, we want them to be entrepreneurs, not bureaucrats doing exactly what they are told from above.

The report emphasised its concern by stating it as a formal finding:

> BP's decentralised management system and entrepreneurial culture have delegated substantial discretion to US refinery managers without clearly defining process safety expectations, responsibilities, or accountabilities.

After the Texas City disaster, BP responded to these concerns by introducing various new positions and some secondary or dotted reporting lines, but it did not alter its fundamental organisational structure.

Consider now the situation at the time of the Gulf of Mexico blowout, depicted in Figure 5.4. BP was divided between upstream and downstream. Upstream refers to exploration and production from oil and gas wells, while downstream refers to oil refineries and gas processing plants, and

---

6 Hopkins, A, *Failure to Learn: the BP Teas City Refinery disaster*, Sydney, CCH, 2008.

7 *The Report of the BP US Refineries Independent Safety Review Panel* (Baker Report), Washington, 2007, pp 92,94; *Investigation Report: Refinery Explosion and Fire* (CSB Report), US Chemical Safety and Hazard Investigation Board, Washington, March 2007, pp 150–51.

the marketing of their products. Upstream and downstream were and are two different worlds.

Upstream was subdivided by geographical area, one such area being the Gulf of Mexico, one of BP's major autonomous business units. Others included the North Sea (UK), Alaska, Russia and so on. There are no other functional heads at this level, for example, there is no senior manager for engineering, or for HSE. This was a critical feature of BP's organisational structure; it meant that the heads of these businesses operated with minimal direction from the corporate centre. Moreover, each geographical area ran its own drilling operations with minimal standardisation from the centre.

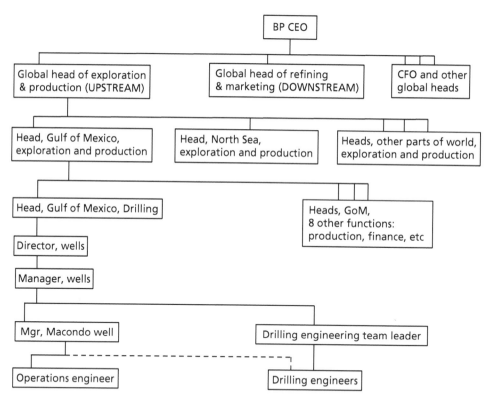

Figure 5.4: Organisational structure for Macondo drilling engineers before disaster

At the next level down, the Gulf of Mexico business is split into nine functional units, one of which is drilling. Notice that the lowly working engineers are still four levels further down. The bottom of the organisational chart is a little more complex than envisaged in the earlier figures. There were two types of engineers at the lowest level. First, an operations engineer who is effectively *owned* by the line manager of the Macondo well. Their potential to exercise independent judgment would have been very limited. Second, there were two drilling engineers who provided services to the manager of the Macondo well, but their boss was an engineering team leader. This would have given them more independence, except that this team leader was directly answerable to the line manager one level up. The way the diagram is drawn gives some indication of how isolated this small group of engineers was from support or input from other parts of the organisation. They were a world unto themselves, except that they were tightly tied to the commercial imperatives of the line they served. This, then, was a highly decentralised organisational structure, meaning there was no control of the engineering function from the corporate centre.

Corresponding to this structure, the decisions made by the engineers reflected to a considerable extent the wishes of the line manager of the Macondo drilling operations, rather than engineering best practice that the engineers would probably have followed had they been more centrally controlled. Other companies told a congressional inquiry they would never have drilled the well the way BP did, and while these statements were somewhat self-serving, there was some truth in them.[8]

It is worth demonstrating the state of mind of these working engineers in more detail. At the completion of drilling, they would need to seal the well at the bottom with cement. The drilling rig, a floating platform, could then move away. Production would come later.

Everyone knew that the way they had chosen to construct the well increased the risk of cement failure. But if successful, it would save the company millions of dollars. If they lost their bet, and the cement failed to seal the well, they would need to spend time and money re-cementing the well. Notice that they assumed uncritically that if the cement job failed they would know about it. In their view, the risk that the cement job might fail was worth taking. One of the engineers wrote in an email that the Macondo line manager was "right on the risk/reward equation",

---

8   Bergen, T, *Spills and Spin*, London, Random House, pp 245–6.

meaning that this was a risk worth taking. Another wrote: "but who cares, it's done, end of story [we] will probably be fine and get a good cement job". These statements were subsequently interpreted by many observers as statements of indifference to *safety* risk. They were not; here's why.

The risk in the minds of the engineers was the risk of having to redo the cement job, and in this matter they were willing to leave the decision to the line manager. They didn't understand that if the cement job failed, they might not even know. That is exactly what happened. The cement job failed, but the subsequent monitoring and testing, which might have revealed the failure, were so inadequate that it was not detected.[9] The result was a catastrophic blowout as the rig prepared to move away. Had these working engineers been under the effective control of an engineering function reporting higher in the organisation, this would not have occurred. They would not have been able to approve a well design that departed so far from good engineering practice, with such a high risk that the cement job would fail, simply to satisfy the cost minimisation pressures uppermost in the minds of line managers.

The point is that there is a clear connection between, on one hand, the organisational structure that subordinated engineers to line management, and on the other, the somewhat careless nature of their engineering decisions, which ended up contributing to the disaster.

BP after Macondo

We can infer that BP itself drew the conclusion I have just drawn because of the radical centralisation it undertook following the accident. The new structure was complex, but it repays study. I focus here on two elements of the new structure — the global well drilling organisation, and a powerful new compliance and assurance organisation known as the safety and operational risk (S&OR) function. The term "operational risk" used by BP refers to the risk of major accident arising from the way a facility or site is being operated. It covers process safety risks, but is not as restrictive a term as process safety. In particular, it covers the risk of blowout which is strictly speaking not a process safety risk.[10]

---

9   See my *Disastrous Decisions*, Chapter 4.

10   For an extensive discussion of meaning of process safety, see *Disastrous Decisions*, Chapters 5 and 6.

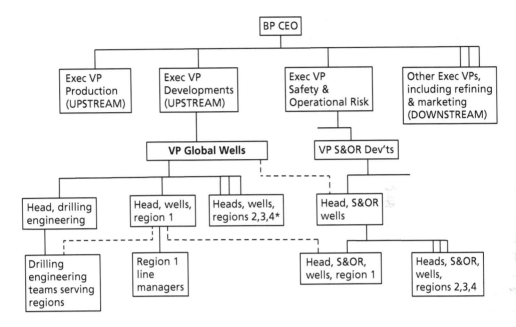

*These regions have reports as for region 1.

Figure 5.5: BP's well drilling function, showing integration with S&OR, post-Macondo

Figure 5.5 is a simplified version of the structure that BP adopted in the year after the Gulf of Mexico accident, as it applied to wells. I have constructed this figure from two presentations given by BP staff at the time.[11] The vice president (VP) of the global well drilling division is in bold near the centre of the diagram. The well drilling organisation answers to an executive VP for developments who is responsible not only for drilling wells but also for the planning of new projects.

---

11 "Managing potential risks in wells", slide presentation Bernard Looney Executive Vice President — Developments, May 2011; "Safety & Operational Risk", slide presentation by Mark R Bly, Executive Vice President, Safety & Operational Risk, May 2011. These presentations provide only a limited amount of data. Figure 5.5 involves some extrapolation from the slides and therefore may not be accurate in every detail. However, it is good enough for present purposes.

This position answers directly to the CEO. It is in this sense that we can speak of the well drilling organisation as centralised or centrally controlled.

The VP of the global wells division has five solid line reports — a head of engineering and four heads of areas or regions of the world in which drilling is taking place. Figure 5.5 focusses on just one of these — region 1. Each area head has line managers as direct reports. The engineering teams are primarily accountable to the head of engineering, but they provide services to the regions. This situation is depicted on the diagram with solid and dotted lines.

The head of engineering does not report to regional leaders but rather to the head of the global wells organisation. This is a structure that minimises the risk that engineering decision-making will be corrupted, as it was at Macondo.

Before considering the role that Safety and Organisational Risk (S&OR) plays in the well drilling organisation, we need some understanding of the way S&OR operates more generally. As can be seen in Figure 5.5, the head of the function answers directly to the CEO. This is an indication of how important this function is to BP. S&OR has two arms — a central arm and a deployed arm. The central arm, based at head office, carries out corporate functions such as audits of the various operations, design of corporate standards, and the development of competence and capability across the corporation. But it is the deployed arm that is important here, for S&OR is far more than a head office activity. Its people are also "embedded" in or "deployed" to the operating organisations. Here they have a day-to-day role in maintaining standards and providing technical expertise. There are several hundred S&OR personal embedded in the upstream production and development (which includes drilling), as well as downstream refining.

How do the S&OR people deployed to the well drilling organisation perform their role? If we focus on the S&OR functional line in Figure 5.5 we see that, two levels down, there is a head (global or worldwide), S&OR, for wells. This position is primarily accountable to superiors in the S&OR function (solid lines). But the position holder also sits on the management team of the VP global wells (dotted line). This means that an S&OR representative takes part in every decision made by this management team. Moreover, their opinion carries particular weight, because in the event of a dispute, they can elevate the matter up the S&OR line.

One level down are the S&OR representatives for well operations in each geographical area or region. Again, they sit on the management team for each area. This means they are not easily overridden by area line managers and if necessary can appeal for support up the S&OR line.

As can be seen, the S&OR function is deeply embedded in well drilling operations. This is an organisational design that maximises the focus on operational excellence.

Parallel observations could be made for the production function in Figure 5.5. The executive VP production heads a large and complex organisation into which S&OR is similarly embedded.

The regional level

The preceding discussion has focused on well drilling operations. In order to get a picture of how this all works, let us refocus at the level of area, that is, geographic region. Somewhat arbitrarily, I focus on BP's operation in Trinidad and Tobago (T&T) because I have relevant data from that region, derived from interviews in 2015.

BP T&T operates 13 production platforms offshore and two terminals onshore. It is a business unit, headed by a country president. As described to me, the following people sit on the executive management team for BP T&T:

- Area head of Legal
- Area head of Community and External Affairs
- Area head of Finance
- Area head of Production
- Area head of Well Drilling
- Area head of S&OR

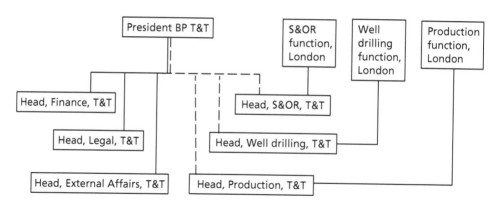

Figure 5.6: BP Trinidad and Tobago, Organisational Structure, Post-Macondo

The first three individuals (heads of Finance, Legal and External Affairs) report exclusively to the country president of BP T&T (see Figure 5.6). This means that they are free to respond to whatever the country president sees as being in the best interests of the T&T business unit. As for the second group of three (the heads of S&OR, Well Drilling and Production), each reports directly to a functional supervisor in London. But each is providing services to the BP T&T business unit, so has a dotted line to the president BP, T&T. This arrangement means that these three are protected from any undue pressure from the business unit to sacrifice operational excellence for the sake of the short-term financial advantage of the business unit.

Let us focus specifically on the S&OR function. There are about 15 S&OR people in Trinidad, all stationed on shore. In other words, no member of the function is deployed full-time to a platform. The group has two purposes: to provide assurance (auditing), and to provide in-depth technical knowledge as required. It consists of operations specialists and technical authorities (TAs). TAs are individuals with certified competency in particular technical disciplines. They are the final arbiters of what is required by the technical standards and whether or not it is reasonable to waive the standards in particular situations. This waiver function is critical. Businesses will from time to time seek a dispensation from a standard on the grounds that compliance is unduly onerous or expensive and that non-compliance does not increase risk appreciably. This may result in pressure to waive a standard, against the better judgment of the individual TA. TAs who sit within the S&OR function are well placed to resist undue pressure. In contrast, TAs scattered throughout a business unit and having other roles within that unit are isolated and have much less support.

The area head of S&OR must visit at least one site each week and do some form of "deep inquiry". For example, if a piece of equipment is not working, and the platform has done an operational risk assessment to establish that it is acceptable to continue operations, the area head of S&OR will review this closely.

If there is disagreement among members of the T&T leadership team, this can usually be resolved with more information. If not, the matter is escalated to a higher level. I was told that this system "works really well".

Box 5.2: A matrix structure

The organisational structure just described can be understood as a "matrix", albeit one that gives greater prominence to the functional dimension than to the business units.

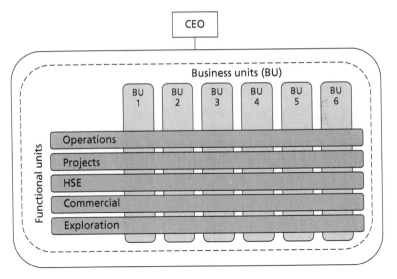

Figure 5.7: A matrix organisational structure

Figure 5.7 is a simplified version of a matrix operated by a number of companies in upstream oil and gas. In this model, the functional heads and the business unit leaders sit together on the CEO's executive leadership team. The specific area functions identified in Figure 5.6 (legal, community and external affairs and finance) do not appear in Figure 5.7; they are taken to be part of the organisational structure of each area business unit.

There is additional symbolism that can be read into Figure 5.7. This particular diagram was used by a petroleum company that was growing by acquisition — acquiring new operations in different parts of the world. Each of these was treated as a new business unit. The company's functional structure was then extended to cover these new businesses, and is therefore depicted as an *overlaying* them.

Matrix organisation is widespread for large organisations in many industries, precisely because it allows companies to operate with multiple business units, as well as centralised control of critical functions.[12] There are many variations of the organisational matrix form, but I shall not dwell on these because it would take us too far afield. Suffice it to say that matters can become extremely complex. For example, Shell operates with a three-dimensional matrix structure![13]

However, one issue deserves further mention. Matrix organisation is often criticised on the grounds that people find themselves serving two masters, with consequent ambiguity about accountabilities. This is potentially a problem where the matrix is truly balanced, giving equal weight to both dimensions. The problem is readily resolved, as

---

12 Hanover Research, Best Practices in Matrix Organisational Structures, December 2013; Bazigos, M and Harter, J, Revisiting the matrix organisation, *McKinsey Quarterly*, January 2016. Here is a concise statement of what a matrix is. It was written in 1978, but stands the test of time. "The identifying feature of a matrix organisation is that some managers report to two bosses rather than to the traditional single boss; there is a dual rather than a single chain of command. Companies tend to turn to matrix forms: 1. when it is absolutely essential that they be highly responsive to two sectors simultaneously, such as markets and technology; 2. when they face uncertainties that generate very high information processing requirements; and 3. when they must deal with strong constraints on financial and/or human resources. Matrix structures can help provide both flexibility and balanced decision making, but at the price of complexity. Matrix organisation is more than a matrix structure. It must be reinforced by matrix systems such as dual control and evaluation systems, by leaders who operate comfortably with lateral decision making, and by a culture that can negotiate open conflict and a balance of power. In most matrix organisations there are dual command responsibilities assigned to functional departments (marketing, production, engineering, and so forth) and to product or market departments. The former are oriented to specialised in-house resources while the latter focus on outputs. Other matrices are split between area-based departments and either products or functions. Every matrix contains three unique and critical roles: the top manager who heads up and balances the dual chains of command, the matrix bosses (functional, product, or area) who share subordinates, and the managers who report to two different matrix bosses. Each of these roles has its special requirements. Aerospace companies were the first to adopt the matrix form, but now companies in many industries (chemical, banking, insurance, packaged goods, electronics, computer, and so forth) and in different fields (hospitals, government)". Davis, S and Lawrence, P, Problems of Matrix Organisations, *Harvard Business Law Review*, May 1978.

13 Grant, R, Organisational Restructuring within the Royal Dutch Shell Group, January 2002.

Jay Galbraith describes in the following passage.[14] Where employees have two bosses,

> The effective practice is to jointly hire, jointly agree on goals, and jointly evaluate performance. These joint decisions result in a unified direction for the person with dual superiors. They also force discussions between the two sides of the matrix and encourage agreement about the general conduct of the business.

In BP's case there is no real ambiguity because the matrix is not balanced. Priority is assigned to the functional line, as indicated by the solid/dotted line convention. BP's organisational structure can therefore be described as an "asymmetric matrix".

Conclusion

The need for organisational restructuring was not the only conclusion BP drew from the Macondo disaster. But it was the most far-reaching and important. It is important because so much else follows from structure. At one point my Trinidadian interviewee told me that "structure builds culture". The reader will no doubt assume that this was in response to a leading question from me. It was not. It was entirely unprompted. He went on to say that in Trinidad there is no culture of observing speed limits, because there are no traffic police. In the US, the contrary is the case, he said. In his mind, the policing of traffic rules was in some sense analogous to the policing of engineering standards. He concluded that the structure we had been discussing had built a culture of operational excellence.

---

14   Galbraith, J, *Designing the Global Corporation*, San Francisco, Jossey-Bass, 2000, p 139.

Chapter 6

What companies do after major accidents

We saw in Chapter 5 how BP reorganised itself after the Gulf of Mexico accident. Companies that have had such a catastrophic experience will almost certainly seek to exercise more centralised control over the operations of their business units. But they do not necessarily adopt the BP model. In this chapter I describe two other centralising responses following a major accident. The first concerns the North American pipeline company, Enbridge, already mentioned in Chapter 3.[1] The second is the response of the multinational resource company, BHP, to the catastrophic failure of a tailings dam used to store mine waste.

Enbridge

2010 was a bad year for the oil and gas industry in the US. It was the year of the Gulf of Mexico blowout. But it was also the year in which two catastrophic pipeline accidents occurred. An underground gas pipeline in San Francisco ruptured, the resulting fire killing eight people, injuring many more and destroying 38 houses. The other pipeline disaster was at Marshall in the state of Michigan. This was an oil pipeline that ruptured, polluting local waterways with vast quantities of sludgy oil coming from the Canadian tar sands thousands of kilometers away. No one was killed or injured but the environmental damage was massive. The cleanup cost more than one billion dollars, making it the most expensive oil spill on land in US history.

The oil pipeline rupture was a watershed event for the pipeline owner, Enbridge. Here is how the company described the situation:

A few years ago, Enbridge believed that we were the industry leader in safety & operational reliability. With the occurrence of our release at Marshall, we will never look at ourselves in the same way again

---

1 Disclosure: I did consultancy work for Enbridge after 2010.

and we recognize that we need to change. Enbridge became the focus of intense public scrutiny with the issuance of the NTSB report on Marshall and the related public fall out has had a material impact on our reputation. Our industry has been caught in the vortex of a significant change in the public's expectation with regard to how pipeline companies operate and the lack of tolerance for ANY incident.[2]

I have already written about the educational campaign that Enbridge embarked on to counteract the psychological biases that contributed to the accident. But Enbridge did much more than that. It had been a largely decentralised company with business units involved in power generation, oil pipelines and gas pipelines, and it now recognised the need for a more disciplined, centralised approach to the management of the major hazards it faced. It set up a central Enterprise Safety and Operational Reliability (ESOR) function with a primary focus on the kinds of risks that could most seriously affect the company. This sounds rather like BP's Safety and Operational Risk (S&OR) function. But there were important differences. To understand the differences, we need to consider the organisational chart. (See Figure 6.1. Note that organisational structures constantly evolve and this chart represents the situation in 2017.)

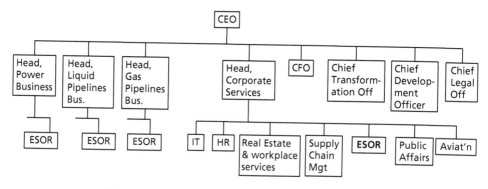

Figure 6.1: Enbridge Organisational Structure[3]

---

2   Enbridge, Why Safety and Operational Reliability is our Top Priority, 2013.

3   www.enbridge.com/About-Us/Executive-Leadership/Byron-Neiles.aspx.

Immediately beneath the CEO on the organisational chart is the eight-member leadership team, consisting of the heads of the three main business units on the left of the CEO, and the corporate function heads on the right. One of these is the head of corporate services. This person has seven different direct reports competing for his attention, one of which is the head of ESOR (in bold). This is the highest-ranking position dedicated to the management of major hazard risks.[4] Here, then, is the first difference from the BP model, where the highest-ranking dedicated risk management position answers directly to the CEO.

Soon after the accident the company had created the position of senior VP for Enterprise Safety and Operational Reliability (ESOR)[5], reporting directly to the CEO, but the position was later downgraded to its current location. Why this was done is not clear, but it may have been a case of designing or redesigning a structure around the people available within the company. This happens all too often and can sometimes lead to suboptimal organisational designs. Whatever the reason, the symbolism is not good; it does not sit well with Enbridge's claim that operational reliability is the number one priority, "not just a core value — safety above all else", as the company's promotional material says.

The corporate ESOR function consists of a team of about 20 people whose job is to set standards, define risk management processes and generally develop the systems by which the business units will manage safety and operational risk. It does not itself carry out audits, risk assessments or management of change processes within the constituent businesses, nor does it have people embedded in those businesses. In these respects, it differs significantly from BP's S&OR function. One other responsibility of the ESOR function is to service Enbridge's Operations and Integrity Committee, which I discuss further in a moment.

Returning to the organisational chart, it will be seen that each of the constituent businesses has an ESOR team. The heads of these teams report to their respective business unit heads, not to the corporate ESOR function, although they have frequent contact with the corporate group. Again,

---

4 The heads of ESOR in the three businesses are arguably at the same level; they are certainly no higher.

5 www.enbridge.com/~/media/CSR/PDFs/chapters/ENB-2013B-CSR-Report-Operational-Risk-Management.pdf.

this is a significant departure from the BP model. On the face of it, then, Enbridge's corporate ESOR function is considerably less powerful that BP's S&OR.

However, Enbridge did not view the creation of the ESOR function as its most important reform. Rather, the focus on enterprise safety and operational reliability was to be driven by a newly created Operations and Integrity Committee.[6] This committee was to be the "central point of accountability". The committee meets once a month and consists of the CEO, representatives of the executive leadership team, including the heads of the business units, and senior safety leaders from across the company, including the head of the corporate ESOR group. It is jointly chaired by the corporate ESOR head and the CEO. The committee is a decision-making body, and the corporate ESOR group has responsibility for ensuring that these decisions are carried out. While the head of ESOR is outranked by the executive members who sit on the committee, he assured me at interview that he was fully able to speak his mind and, moreover, that he set the committee's agenda. In any case, there was little disagreement on the committee because its members had lived through the Marshall disaster and remained very aware of the need to manage these risks effectively, he said.

The creation of an Operations and Integrity Committee serviced by the corporate ESOR group amounts to an alternative response to disaster, alternative, that is, to BP's matrix model. It does not require the creation of new positions in the company (other than the creation of a group to service the committee and administer its decisions) nor does it involve any rearrangement of personal accountabilities. The committee is a grouping of existing positions designed to enhance the salience of ESOR in the company.

It is hard to assess whether Enbridge's committee model is likely to be as effective as BP's matrix strategy. However, it does seem to be more vulnerable to change, in particular, to decay. Committees can meet less frequently, or simply cease to meet, without the need for any formal organisational change, whereas a matrix requires explicit organisational rearrangements, if is to be abandoned. This is not to say that a matrix

---

6   www.enbridge.com/projects-and-infrastructure/public-awareness/line-5-michigan/
    system-wide-safety-enhancements.

structure is unchangeable, but it cannot just fall into disuse in the way that a committee can.

Of course, Enbridge's organisational response to disaster is unlikely to suffer this fate any time soon. The company is under intense public scrutiny especially in Michigan, where higher standards are being demanded of it. Public opinion[7] has forced the company to reposition a pipeline in the Great Lakes, so as to reduce the risk of rupture and catastrophic pollution.[7] These external political pressures, as Enbridge has noted, have changed the way the company must manage risk for the foreseeable future.

BHP and Samarco

In 2015, BHP suffered a devastating accident in Brazil, at the Samarco iron ore mine it co-owns with Brazilian company, Vale. A large "tailings" dam disintegrated, releasing a torrent of muddy mine waste. Nineteen people died — it could have been many more had it occurred at a different time of day. Villages were engulfed, and the pollution of the river downstream damaged the livelihood of many thousands of people all the way to the sea, 400 miles away. This was the worst environmental disaster of its kind in Brazil's history. BHP has already paid out billions of dollars and the final cost may be a lot more. Some of its officers are facing prosecution on manslaughter charges. It was an accident that rocked the company and forced a re-think of some of the ways it did business.[8] Just prior to publication of this book, Vale suffered a second tailings dam disaster, at Brumadinho, not far from the Samarco site.[9] However, BHP was not involved, and this second disaster will not be discussed here.

Samarco was not BHP's first tailings disaster. In 1984, a tailings dam failed at the Ok Tedi gold and copper mine in a remote part of Papua New Guinea.[10] The dam was not rebuilt, and the discharge from ongoing mining

---

7   www.uppermichiganssource.com/content/news/State-of-Michigan-Enbridge-enter-into-Line-5-agreement-460291903.html.

8   Kiernan, P, Engineer Warned Samarco Over Dam That Burst, *Wall Street Journal (Eastern ed)* 19 January 2016; Kiernan, P, Brazilian Mine Report Is Criticized, *Wall Street Journal (Eastern ed)* 30 August 2016.

9   www.wsj.com/articles/deadly-brazil-mine-accident-puts-waste-dams-in-spotlight-11548874428

10 www.aph.gov.au/binaries/library/pubs/cib/1995–96/96cib04.pdf.

operations led to a major environmental disaster, disrupting the lives of 50,000 villagers downstream.

Tailings dams are a neglected, but high-risk aspect of mining. Tailings are the waste material resulting from the initial separation of the commercially valuable substance from the rock and other material that comes with it. The tailings are often transported by water and deposited in a land fill area that has been surrounded by low earth walls to contain the slurry. The water is intended to drain away or evaporate leaving the dry waste behind. The walls can then be heightened to accommodate the inflow of further tailings. In this way tailings dams can rise to great heights. The tallest tailings dams, at copper mines in the Peruvian Andes, are already as tall as Hoover Dam and have permits to rise even further. Obviously, such dams need to be designed with the utmost care. Too often, they are not.[11]

There are variations on the tailings dam theme. In UK coal mines, the refuse material was often dumped in great "slag" heaps, sometimes on hillsides with villages down below at the bottom of the valley. In 1966, the Welsh village of Aberfan was partially destroyed when one of these slag heaps gave way after heavy rain. Twenty-six adults and 116 school children died when the school was engulfed.[12]

The problem is that tailings dams (and slag heaps) are often overlooked when companies are considering the risks of their operations. For underground operations, the most serious hazards are assumed to be underground, and what happens on the surface at the end of the mining process is dealt with as an afterthought, if at all. Even for surface mining operations, the focus of attention is on the hazards of the production process, with the hazards of waste disposal sometimes receiving short shrift.

An Australian underground coal mining company was so oblivious to these risks that it allowed a tailings pondage to develop on a steep hillside above a world heritage river. The pondage finally gave way, polluting the river below, for which the company was heavily fined.[13] What was most

11 For a further discussion of this problem see Golder Associates, *Review of Tailings Management Guidelines and Recommendations for Improvement,* submitted to International Council on Mining and Metals (ICMM), December 2016.

12 McLean, I, and Johnes, M *Aberfan: Government and Disasters,* Cardiff, Welsh Academic Press, 2000.

13 www.abc.net.au/news/2017-07-14/clarence-colliery-fined-one-million-for-blue-mountains-spill/8709834

upsetting to this company was that despite its carefully developed risk management system, this risk had slipped through unnoticed.

The consequences of this neglect are striking. Experts estimate that each year there are between one and four tailings dam failures worldwide. This is roughly ten times the failure rate of water storage dams. According to one expert, "our tailings dams and dumps are among the highest-risk structures on Earth."[14]

So how did BHP manage the risk of tailings dam failure at Samarco before the accident? To answer this question, we need to know something about the mine's ownership structure.[15] The mine dates back at least to the 1970s. At that time, it was Brazilian owned. It was subsequently sold to Utah International and thence to General Electric. In 1984 BHP bought in, and ended up with 49% share of the Samarco mine. Finally, in 2000, Samarco became a 50-50 joint venture between BHP and Vale. As this account makes clear, the mine had had a series of owners. Furthermore, these various owners would have had relatively little interest in how the mine was operated, as long as it operated profitably.

The BHP-Vale joint venture is a so-called Non-Operated Joint Venture (NOJV). This meant Samarco operated more or less independently from BHP, except that BHP (and Vale) supplied directors who sat on the Samarco company board.

The short answer to the question, then, is that BHP itself did not manage the risk of tailing dam failure. That was left to Samarco, which evidently failed to manage this risk effectively. Clearly, the concept of a NOJV has proved problematic for BHP. As a joint owner of Samarco, it was legally liable if things went disastrously wrong. Yet it did not take responsibility for managing the catastrophic risks to which it was exposed.

To understand BHP's response, we must first sketch its organisational structure. See Figure 6.2. The shaded boxes in this figure were added *after* the Samarco accident and should be ignored for the moment.

---

14   Kiernan, P, Dangers Loom in Mining Dams - Engineers warn of risks from massive structures formed after years of rapid industry growth, *Wall Street Journal (Eastern ed)* 5 April 2016.

15   www.bhp.com/-/media/bhp/documents/investors/reports/2007/samarcopresentationsouth americansitevisit.pdf?la=en.

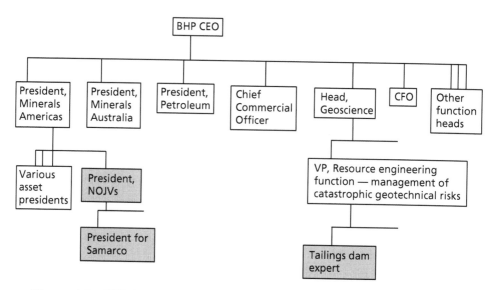

Figure 6.2: BHP Organisational Chart — aspects. Changes after Samarco accident in grey[16]

The company has three major producing divisions: Minerals Americas, Minerals Australia and Petroleum.[17] Its executive leadership team[18] consists of the heads of these three divisions, plus some other specialised functional heads — a chief financial officer, a chief commercial officer, a head of geoscience and so on.

The response to Samarco was two-fold. First, BHP has modified its approach to NOJVs, of which it has several in South America. It grouped them together as the "NOJV asset" and positioned this as one of the assets in its Minerals Americas region (see Figure 6.2).[19] The president of this asset now has direct subordinates who sit on the boards of the various NOJVs, including one on the Samarco board. In this way, BHP hopes to tie the NOJVs more tightly into one of its main operations groups.

---

16 Source: www.bhp.com/our-approach/our-company/leadership-team; plus interviews.

17 BHP website, February 2018.

18 www.bhp.com/our-approach/our-company/leadership-team, 2 February 2018.

19 For BHP, asset refers to commodity type within a particular region. For example, within the Americas group there will be a president for coal, one for copper and so on. The three regional groups are not independent businesses; their marketing is done for them by the Chief Commercial Officer's function.

Second, and most significantly from point of view of this book, BHP acted to recognise tailings dam failure as one of the catastrophic risks that it needed to manage centrally, rather than leaving it to mine sites, whether they be NOJVs, or BHP-operated mine sites. The company already had a central "resource engineering function" to deal with catastrophic geotechnical risks. It enlarged this function to include tailings dams and recruited a tailings dam expert and team to constitute a tailings dam function within the larger resource engineering function (see Figure 6.2).

Here is BHP's description:

> A centralised function for dams and tailings governance and risk management has been created, to support our site management to apply appropriate dam risk management practices and build internal capability across the Group.

The statement went on:

> We have investigated potential technological solutions for better dam management, in conjunction with leading technology providers. We have identified monitoring and early warning as having the greatest potential to enhance dam risk controls in the near term. We are also examining the feasibility of additional technologies to further enhance controls for dams.[20]

BHP's "resource engineering function" sits under the head of geoscience, one of BHP's top executive leadership positions. This means that tailings dam management is now part of a function that runs all the way to the top of the corporation. In principle, then, if the tailing dam expert fails to get cooperation from sites operating tailings dams, the matter can be escalated all the way to the executive leadership team for resolution. This is a big step towards centralised control of tailings dam risk.

It should be noted that not all BHP's catastrophic risks are covered by the resource engineering function. Nor are they the responsibility of any other central function. It is apparent that the centralising impetus provided by the Samarco disaster extended only to dam management. It did not cause a redesign of BHP's whole approach to catastrophic risk management. This point will be elaborated in Chapter 7.

---

20   www.bhp.com/environment/dams-and-tailings-management.

Observe, finally, there is no one on the executive team with specific responsibility for other areas of HSE (Health Safety and Environment). BHP's reasoning is that HSE is a line management responsibility and corporate HSE staff are viewed as a resource to line managers, not an independent function with management responsibilities.

Conclusion

The centralisation of catastrophic risk management that occurred at BP after its Gulf of Mexico accident was the most thorough and complete of all the cases discussed in this book. Perhaps this is because the accident was a near-death experience for BP; it nearly destroyed the company. The two accidents discussed in this chapter were extremely costly for the companies concerned, but they did not threaten their very existence. Perhaps for this reason, these accidents did not give rise to such a complete organisational transformation. Nevertheless, in both cases the companies responded by setting in place structures that enabled them to exercise greater control from the centre over the management of some or all the catastrophic risks to which they were exposed.

This is a quite general phenomenon. I recall speaking at a drilling company conference a couple of years after the Gulf of Mexico blowout. The drilling company had grown by acquisition and consisted of a series of quasi-independent drilling businesses bound together loosely at the top. I spoke about one of the drilling practices on the Deepwater Horizon drilling rig that had contributed to Gulf of Mexico disaster. I asked the Chief Operating Officer (COO) whether this was the practice in his company. He didn't know, so he put the question to the audience. It turned out it was indeed the practice in some of the businesses he oversaw. This was something of a light bulb moment for the COO, reinforcing his view that the company needed stronger risk control from the centre.

The reaction of companies like BP, Enbridge and BHP when disaster strikes is exactly the kind of response recommended by experts in the accident reports discussed in Chapter 2. Clearly these companies believe that when it comes to the crunch, cultural change — change in "the way we do things around here" — requires structural change.

Chapter 7

Applying the concept of organisational structure

Some of my consultancy work has been about applying the general concept of organisational structure to particular situations. This has enabled me to understand why the organisation found itself in trouble, as well as to suggest solutions. This chapter looks at several of these cases in order to demonstrate just how widely applicable these ideas are.

I deal with the following four cases:

- the Australian Air Force, which experienced a health disaster affecting its aircraft maintenance workers

- a metalliferous mine which suffered a catastrophic cave-in

- a minerals processing company that was failing to manage process safety effectively, and

- a chemical company, whose board-initiated major hazard risk audits were being censored before reaching the board.

Each of these cases highlights a different aspect of organisational structure.

The first concerns the need for a specialised, independent, high-status technical regulatory authority, much as was recommended by the *Columbia* Accident Investigation Board, discussed in Chapter 2.

The second focuses on the circumstances of a technical professional who is located at too low a position in the hierarchy and is unable to get senior management to take seriously his technically-based concerns about the possibility of a mine cave-in.

The third is about a global company that is managing catastrophic risk in a decentralised way, exactly as BP was doing prior to its Gulf of Mexico accident.

The fourth is about a board's attempt to use an audit process to inform itself about the effectiveness of its risk management system, and how this was thwarted by the organisational location of the safety risk auditor.

Australian Air Force[1]

In the latter part of the 20th century, the Australian Air Force experienced
a major health disaster. Hundreds of Air Force personnel were exposed to
toxic chemicals that permanently ruined their health. The exposure took
place over a period of years at Amberley Air Force base in Queensland,
where maintenance personnel were required to work inside the fuel tanks
of F-111 aircraft. Many visited the medical centre at the base complaining
of non-specific symptoms such as skin irritation, memory loss, headaches,
gastrointestinal problems, loss of interest in sex and so on. Unfortunately,
doctors treated the symptoms without inquiring into the causes, and
nothing effective was done until finally one of the doctors took it upon
himself to investigate. This led rapidly to a realisation of the extent of the
problem and the suspension of the maintenance program. I should say,
in passing, that the doctors who failed to recognise the problem cannot
reasonably be held accountable for this failure. None had been trained in
occupational medicine and they worked on contract, being paid for the
number of number of clients they saw. There was no expectation that they
visit workplaces to understand what might be the causes of the symptoms
they were encountering. I was invited onto a board inquiring into what
had happened and why it had been allowed to continue over such a long
period.

The board soon became aware of an extraordinary contrast. We found that
air safety, that is the safety of aircraft and air crews, was handled rigorously
and very effectively, while the management of ground safety — the safety
of maintenance workers and other support people — was woefully poor.
The routine exposure of F-111 maintenance workers to toxic chemicals
was an example of this *relative* indifference to the welfare of people on
the ground. Explaining this difference was the key to understanding
the experience of the maintenance workers. It also enabled us to make
appropriate recommendations.

What we had observed was an organisational culture that emphasised air
safety, but not ground safety. There was a highly effective set of practices
aimed at achieving air safety, for example, an excellent and well used
aviation safety occurrence reporting system and rigorous maintenance

---

1   Hopkins, A, *Safety Culture and Risk*, Sydney, CCH, 2005.

practices with respect to the safety of the aircraft. There were no similar practices in relation to the safety of ground crews.

The immediate explanation for this difference lay in the structure of the organisation. In a large organisation like the Air Force, cultural themes such as safety are only likely to be prominent if the organisation has agencies or functions within it that have specific responsibility for these matters. The better resourced these agencies, and the higher the status of their heads, the more prominent the themes. Two agencies, in particular, ensured that air safety had the highest priority. One of these focused on the activities of the aviators themselves — the Directorate of Flying Safety — and the other on the mechanical safety of aircraft — the Directorate General of Technical Airworthiness. Both were headed by senior officers. These officers did not have safety as just one of their responsibilities; it was their exclusive focus. In structuring itself in this way, the Air Force ensured that air safety would be effectively championed at a senior level and that a culture of air safety would be effectively promoted. However, there was no corresponding agency or leader responsible for ground safety. It was therefore to be expected that ground safety would have a low priority. Viewed in this light, the Air Force failure to protect its maintenance workers from toxic chemicals is no surprise. The failure was an outcome of the way the Air Force was organised.

Accordingly, we recommended the establishment of a new ground safety agency to be headed by a senior officer of the same rank as the head of the flying safety agency. The Air Force indeed set up a ground safety agency, but it did not accept our recommendation about the status of its head — the new head was appointed at a lower level. In so doing, the Air Force missed the point of our analysis and perpetuated the existing priority of air safety.

Of course, in inquiries of this nature, each answer begets a further question. Given that the cultural difference between air and ground safety can be attributed to differences in organisational structure, we can ask: why had the Air Force organised itself in this way? The answer to this lies outside the Air Force, in the wider community. Air safety had not always been good. Indeed, the Air Force was in crisis in the early 1990s when there were 14 military aircraft crashes in a two-year period, resulting in the loss of 23 lives. Public opinion demanded that something be done, and the Air Force reorganised itself in response. It is always helpful to trace the causes of cultures to sources outside an organisation in this way, as it will often provide clues as to why things are the way they are and why it may be difficult to change them. It will probably take a public relations disaster of equal magnitude to the air crashes and fatalities of the 1990s to ensure that ground safety is given the same priority.

A metalliferous mine

A metalliferous mine, that is a hard rock mine, suffered a major underground rock fall. No one was killed or injured, but mining was interrupted for months. The mine was owned by a multinational mining company. It was the jewel in the company's crown and the interruption cost the company dearly. Accordingly, it set up an incident investigation team to understand what had gone wrong. The team was chaired by a senior company manager, who wrote the report. I was invited onto the team to give an organisational perspective.

The mining method was to break-up the ore body using explosives and transport it to the surface, leaving large underground caverns, which would later be filled in. Provided the rock surrounding a cavern was solid, the roof formed a natural arch which prevented cave-ins. But if the caverns were too close together, the ability of the surrounding rock to support the roof was reduced, leading to a greater risk of collapse. This was the most significant risk the mine faced. It was therefore vital that the size of the blocks to be extracted and the sequence of extraction be carefully risk assessed. This was the job of the geotechnical specialists. If they failed to do their job properly, or if their advice was not heeded, people might die. As someone told the inquiry, the job of the geotechs was to keep the managers out of jail.

Unfortunately, though, the head geotech did not have sufficient organisational clout. He reported to the mine's head of planning, who sat on the mine's senior management team. The head of planning was responsible for designing the production sequence so as to maximise production, while also managing the risk of cave-in. He was thus the "point of aggregation" between the geotechs, who naturally erred on the side of caution, and the production planners, whose aim was to maximise production. The head planner's job was to balance these competing pressures.

As mining progressed, the mine was slowly running out of blocks that could be easily mined. But the economic pressures were relentless, and the planners chose a mining sequence which led ultimately to failure. The geotech specialist had felt uneasy about the mining plan. "If I'd had my way", he told the inquiry, "I would have changed the mining sequence". He'd had a "gut feeling" he said, that the proposed sequence was not sound. His concern was based on geotechnical experience, but not hard data — professional judgments about risk seldom are. This meant that he was easily overridden. The inquiry asked the head of planning why he had not paid greater attention to the geotech's concerns. His response was that he "could not talk to the business on the basis of a gut feeling".

What is clear from this account is that if the head geotech specialist had been higher in the organisational structure, his concern would have been more difficult to ignore. Indeed, given the right organisational structure he would have been in a position to veto the proposed mining sequence. My advice was that the head of the geotech group should be one step up in the organisational hierarchy, to ensure that his "voice" carried greater authority. That seemed to me a modest proposal in the circumstances. However, the chair of the inquiry panel was uneasy about making a recommendation that might be unacceptable to the top leadership of the company. Instead, the words he used in the report were as follows:

> _**The influence of the geotechnical function needs to be strengthened:**_ the investigation team identified through numerous interviews that the geotechnical team's voice is not strong enough and that their concerns are diluted under the production pressures and priorities (italics and underlining in the original).

This certainly captured our concern, but it fell short of the particular recommendation I had urged that we make. Notice that the above recommendation echoed my use of the word "voice", which I intended to be somewhat metaphoric. However, the vagueness of the above wording allowed the mine to adopt a more literal interpretation. It chose to strengthen the voice of the head geotech by providing him with assertiveness training! In so doing it provided a very individualised solution to what was essentially an issue of organisational structure.

It is common for senior officers to translate organisational issues into personal failures in this way. It is usually much easier to offer training than to tackle the challenge of organisational change. But unless this challenge is confronted head on, problems are likely to recur.

A mineral processing company

The process safety advisor for a global mineral processing company asked me to run some process safety workshops for managers at various company sites around the world. (Remember: process safety is about retaining control of the process, so that explosive, toxic and otherwise dangerous substances remain properly contained.) The company's sites operated as largely independent business units, and there was no one at corporate headquarters with responsibility for process safety, and the authority to ensure it was being managed effectively. In particular, the process safety advisor was just that, an advisor, and he had to negotiate with each business unit to run my workshop at site. During these workshops, I spoke about the need to think and behave differently in relation to process safety, and also about the need to structure the company differently, so as to give process safety greater salience. The audiences were open to ideas about thinking and behaving differently, but they regarded the structure of their company as adequate, and my arguments for structural change fell on deaf ears. A couple of years later the company employed another process safety management consultant who visited some of the same sites at which I had spoken. This man was a colleague of mine, and comparing notes, it was apparent that nothing much had changed in the way they did things.

During my series of workshops, I had discovered that various sites were unaware of major accidents occurring at other company sites operating very similar technologies. They were, therefore, similarly at risk. Centralised control of process safety would have meant that lessons painfully learnt at one site would be effectively passed on and implemented at other sites, before they suffered a similar incident. However, the company was not ready at that time to take this step.

Nevertheless, top management at the company was slowly becoming aware of the issue of process safety. Its principal organisational strategy for dealing with process safety was to create a Process Safety Directorate. This consisted of the general managers of the operations with the greatest process safety risks, plus one or two other executive leadership team members. This was intended to be a high-powered team. However, its authority was very limited. This can be seen in the mission and charter for the Directorate where the following statements are made:

It is important that the management of process safety risk remains with the line....

What the Directorate is NOT accountable for:

- The Directorate does not participate in the implementation activity which resides with and is the responsibility of the business unit

- The Directorate does not directly organise or carry out audits

- Additional guidelines necessary to support the implementation of process safety management and control procedures may be needed from time to time. Such guidelines will be produced by Group HSE (Health Safety and Environment) in consultation with the business units, with the Directorate involved only in approving the final products

- The Directorate does not directly supply training and other direct assistance to business.

The charter, in other words, envisaged a very limited role for the Process Safety Directorate. It had no authority to intervene in the business units and no role in ensuring that business units were in compliance with standards relevant to process safety. Although a central organ of the company, it did not exercise centralised control in any way.

The company's position was that responsibility for process safety remained with the line. While that statement is unobjectionable, it is not enough. There is often a conflict between the business goals of line managers, which include minimising costs, and the requirements of process safety that may require considerable expenditure. The strategy of making line managers accountable for process safety in effect internalises this conflict within each manager. It is a system that buries the conflict and increases the risk that managers will compromise process safety for the sake of profit (regardless of how principled individual managers may be). The solution to this problem is to embed in the organisation people whose primary concern is process safety. They can then put the case for process safety expenditure to relevant line managers, bringing issues out into the open. These decisions may need to be escalated, which means that process safety experts need to be organised into an independent function that runs upwards within the corporation as far as possible. All this has been canvassed already and will not be discussed further here.

One of the business units I visited experienced a major accident (without fatalities) just prior to my visit; it had a very similar accident a couple of years later. One might conclude from this that leaving responsibility with line management, without any other checks and balances, was not achieving the desired effect. I was left with the feeling that this company would not take matters much further until it had suffered a catastrophic event that killed numerous people and did real financial damage to the company.

Much later, the process safety advisor who had organised my first series of workshops asked me to think about another series we could offer, as a follow-up to the first. I thought long and hard about this but eventually decided that until the company was ready to adopt the structural arrangements I had suggested, there was little point in having another round of workshops.

There is an interesting twist to this story. The company's board became aware of what is probably the single most widely recognised lesson of BP's Texas City refinery disaster. An explosion at a process unit at that refinery killed 15 people who were working in temporary office blocks located much too close to the process unit. The lesson was that flimsily constructed buildings should be located well away from potential explosion sources. Moreover, buildings in which people worked which were necessarily close to explosion sources should be explosion-proof. The board of the minerals processing company gave orders that all its sites should implement this lesson, and that centrally provided funds would be available for this if necessary. In this matter, then, the risk was to be managed centrally. The board did not recognise, however, that all of its catastrophic risks needed to be managed centrally.

The failure of a corporate assurance function

An Australian chemical company was in difficulty. Its senior leadership was not transmitting concerns about major hazard and regulatory risk to its board. This in itself is not uncommon. Unfortunately, however, the board's corporate audit function was not working well. This audit group was supposed to be independent of line management and to report directly to the board. To this end, it could bypass the most senior executives and reach down into the organisation to discover what was really going on. But it was not working as intended: the board and the CEO were not getting the bad news.

Here's why. The safety risk auditor in this group did not report directly to the board. Instead he reported to the head of the corporate audit group, a financial auditor by profession. The latter's role was to summarise matters raised by the safety risk auditor for board presentations. In the process, the most disturbing findings were invariably omitted. It would not be unreasonable to say that he was censoring the message.

The safety auditor carried out detailed audits every three months of major hazard risks faced by the company. These audits were coming up with alarming findings, such as the fact that some pressure vessels were beyond their inspection dates by as much as 15 years. In this case, the operators of the pressure vessels believed that the company could not afford financially to shut down the operation to carry out the necessary checks. The safety risk auditor believed that this kind of information should be made available to the board, so it could evaluate the risk for itself. However, the head auditor would not pass on these and other concerns to the board. On one occasion, the stated reason was that the head of the business unit that had been audited was making a presentation to the board about how well they were managing major hazard risk, and the head auditor did not want to undermine this presentation. More generally, his view was that information should not go to the board unless it was "board-ready". His concern was that anything that went to the board in writing might later be "discoverable", if the company had a serious incident, and he saw it as his job to protect board members from personal liability. In short, the safety auditor was completely blocked from performing his function by the organisational position in which he found himself.

The head auditor's position involves a misunderstanding of the law. Work health and safety law in Australia requires directors to be proactive in seeking out bad news. If a board sets up an audit committee but passively accepts its assurances that all is well, directors remain potentially liable should things go badly wrong.[2] The head auditor was therefore not doing the board a favour by protecting it from bad news. Of course, if a board receives bad news but does nothing about it, and an accident ensues, board

---

2   Tooma, M, *Due Diligence: Duty of Officers*, Sydney, CCH, 2012.

members may be in a worse position, but if they act conscientiously on the bad news, their liability is minimised.

It is easy to see this story as a conflict between individuals — the safety auditor and his immediate boss — but again, this would miss the point. It was the safety auditor's subordinate organisational position that enabled his reports to be censored. The solution would have been a simple organisational change — to allow the safety auditor to report directly to the board.

There were other structural aspects of this problem. Most strikingly, the head auditor formally reported directly to the chief financial officer, who in turn reported to the CEO. This arrangement thoroughly undermined the board's audit process, which in principle was designed to give the board an independent line of sight down into the business.

Second, the practice of the head auditor was to consult with the audited parties to ensure that as far as possible they concurred with the findings of safety audits. This potentially overrode the safety auditor and inevitably blunted the initial message.

The conclusion is very clear. The board's major hazard risk audit process had been compromised by the structural position of the auditor. Boards that want an independent view of how well their companies are performing need to devise a structure that will deliver the necessary degree of independence to their auditors.

Internal auditors are sometimes blamed for not being sufficiently independent and courageous in raising "red flags" with company boards. According to one critic, "they need to step up."[3] Unfortunately this misses the point. Too often, the organisational structure prevents them from "stepping up", and it takes truly exceptional courage and willingness to risk one's job to get the message to the board.

Board responsibility

This case also suggests the need for organisational change at board level. In the UK, a so-called Process Safety Leadership Group has made a remarkable

---

3   www.abc.net.au/news/2018-05-22/banking-royal-commission-auditors-need-to-lift-their-game/
    9786218;   www.iia.org.au/sf_docs/default-source/sopac-2018/kn2---why-organisational-culture-
    matters-(elizabeth-johnstone).pdf?sfvrsn=2.

statement about the role that company boards should ideally play in the management of process safety. It is entitled, "Principles of Process Safety Leadership" [4] and it is signed by the CEOs of several industry associations and as well as various government agencies responsible for the regulation of health, safety and the environment. [5] It includes the following requirement:

> At least one board member should be fully conversant in process safety management in order to advise the board of the status of process safety risk management within the organisation and of the process safety implications of board decisions.

Notice that this board member has an active role to play, in particular, "to advise the board on the status of process safety risk management within the organisation". To do this effectively, the director would need to communicate directly with the process safety auditor and could not be satisfied with a summary and second-hand version provided by a head auditor whose expertise was finance. This would strengthen the voice of the process safety auditor enormously.

The preceding recommendation echoes one made by the US Chemical Safety Board following the BP Texas City refinery disaster. Its recommendation was for the appointment of

> An additional non-executive director of the board of directors with specific professional expertise and experience in refinery operations and process safety.[6]

The appointment of a director with particular expertise and tasked with advising the board about how well major hazards are being managed is the kind of organisational change that would make a significant difference to the culture of the organisation with respect to the management of these hazards.

Conclusion

These cases demonstrate the flexibility of the notion of organisational structure and the way it can be deployed in a wide variety of situations,

---

4 www.hse.gov.uk/comah/buncefield/pslgprinciples.pdf.

5 See also Hackitt, J, *Why Corporate Governance and Why Now?*, OECD Corporate Governance for Process Safety Conference, 14–15 June 2012.

6 Quoted in Hopkins, 2008, op cit, p 105.

both to explain what has happened and to provide solutions. It is a powerful perspective that deserves much wider application.

However, unless a company is in crisis, recommending changes to organisational structure is likely to be met with resistance. Existing organisational structures embody systems of power and status and those that benefit from the existing structures will not welcome change. As I have already said, but it bears repeating, it is much easier for top managers to see problems as stemming from the deficiencies of individuals, rather than to attribute them to organisational structures. That way a problem can be dealt with by some additional training or if need be, by replacing the individual. This is the classic, rotten-apple-in-the-barrel approach: remove the rotten apple and you've solved the problem.

I have often heard top managers say that organisational structure is a secondary issue. The important thing is to make sure you have appointed the right person for the job. I am told that an exceptional person will find a way to overcome whatever structural obstacles there may be. And while that may be true, it is clearly better to have an organisational structure that supports people in their jobs, rather than throwing up obstacles for them to overcome.

Chapter 8

How decentralisation undermines process safety: some illuminating cases

Andrew Hopkins and Gilsa Pacheco Monteiro

This book is addressed to multiple audiences. One of the primary aims has been to avoid overloading the general reader with too much technical detail. However, technical detail can enrich our understanding immeasurably. This chapter therefore ventures into greater detail. It is written to be intelligible to general readers and we hope that they will find it illuminating. It is also written for people who manage hazardous technologies and wish to understand more fully what is at stake.

The chapter presents three examples in which it is clear that a decentralised organisational structure undermined process safety. It is based on PhD field work carried out by a process safety engineer with long experience in the upstream oil and gas industry. For this reason, it is jointly authored. It represents the collaboration of a sociologist and an engineer.

In all three cases, autonomous business units in a decentralised company took risk management decisions, without any input from the corporate risk management function and without its knowledge. In all three cases these decisions authorised substandard practices. And in all three cases these substandard practices had negative consequences for the business units concerned. Finally, we provide evidence that had these decisions been taken by process safety experts within the central risk management function, they would have been different, and the negative consequences would have been avoided. These three cases are therefore a powerful demonstration of the validity of the central argument of the book.

Case 1: The failure to flare

The first case concerns a request for an exemption from the standards produced by engineers in the corporate centre. The exemption was requested by managers for a particular operation in one the business units of the company. This is a critical issue, as explained in Chapter 2. To repeat what was said there, centrally determined engineering standards are sometimes thought to be inappropriate or unnecessarily burdensome in particular situations. When this happens, the people concerned will seek to have the standard waived in the particular case. The vital question is: who is authorised to grant such an exemption or waiver? In a centrally controlled organisation it will be a technically competent engineer in the central function. In a decentralised organisation it is likely to be a line manager in the business unit concerned. Such a manager is under commercial pressure to grant the waiver and is therefore not in a position to make an unbiased decision. In this way, substandard procedures can become the norm in the business unit.

In the case in question, drilling rigs were contracted from time to time to perform maintenance operations on existing, onshore oil wells. In one of these operations, a fluid stream from the bottom of the well, consisting of water, gas, oil and debris was brought to the surface for separation of its components. According to a company technical standard, if the gas to oil ratio was above a certain threshold value, the gas posed an explosion risk and it had to be separated from the remaining fluid and taken to a flare system to be safely ignited (flared) — see Figure 8.1.

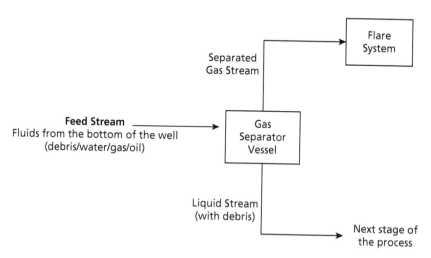

Figure 8.1: Gas separation and flare system

The gas separator vessel and flare system were detachable and portable, and the contract specified that the drilling contractor maintain a certain number these systems at the support base, for use when the gas threshold was exceeded.

However, when the corporate engineering group reviewed the standard, they decided it was not sufficiently stringent. Gas separation and flaring was made a requirement, regardless of how low the gas to oil ratio was.

The contractor apparently had sufficient gas separators to meet the increased demand under the new standard, but not a sufficient number of flare systems. The business unit could have re-negotiated the contract to provide for an increased number of flares. This would have ensured compliance with the revised technical standard. But instead, it chose to exempt the operations from the technical standard, as it was entitled to do, provided it carried out a risk assessment. Operating without the necessary flare system meant releasing the flammable gas direct to atmosphere. The risk assessment should have involved a study of where the gas would be released, how it might disperse and alternatively where it might accumulate, what potential ignition points there were in the vicinity and so on. None of this was done. Instead, the chosen risk management strategy was to use portable gas detectors to monitor gas concentrations and to stop operations if the gas concentration rose above a certain point. This is an inherently unreliable system because it depends on humans to deploy the gas monitors and to respond to any gas alarms that might occur.

But the situation was even worse than this. The previous standard specified that a flare system be used whenever the gas to oil ratio was above the threshold. After the new standard came into effect, the business chose to exempt itself from the flare requirement *even when the ratio exceeded that threshold*, relying on the portable monitoring system to protect against gas buildups. Thus, while engineers in the central function had sought to tighten the standard, the business itself had conducted a risk assessment that allowed it to relax the standard further. This is a particularly glaring example of what can happen in a decentralised organisation. It is clear that if the central engineering function had been involved at the business unit level, it would never have authorised a procedure that released gas without flaring it.

But to continue the story, based on the new risk management strategy of monitoring gas concentrations, the business began routinely to carry out this operation without a flare, even with gas levels above the originally specified threshold. After the new standard was issued, four such exemptions were granted in a two-month period. The new, substandard procedure had been thoroughly normalised.

However, things went badly wrong after the fourth such exemption. Two hours after a maintenance operation began, a flammable vapour cloud formed and ignited, leading to a fire that severely injured two operators. For some unknown reason, gas monitoring was not being carried out that day, as it should have been according to the business's alternative risk management procedures. This allowed the vapour cloud to accumulate undetected. The business's preferred risk reduction measure, which relied on human intervention in a critical situation, had failed.

These events are a dramatic demonstration of how decentralised decision-making can lead to inadequate risk management. Conversely, it is clear that if the central risk function had been in charge or granting exemptions, this substandard practice could not have developed, and the incident would never have happened.

Case 2: The removal of backup pumps

The second case involves a comparison between two petroleum production facilities in the company. Both sites were equipped with pumps to provide water for emergency firefighting. In each case a backup pump was available. As shown in Figure 8.2, the pump configurations at the two sites were different. The reason for the design differences is not known but both systems had the necessary degree of backup (redundancy).

Facility A had two pumps, each capable of providing 100% of the water needed for firefighting, so if one pump failed, the other could do the job. Facility B had three pumps each capable of providing 50% of the required water. To fight a fire, two pumps needed to operate. If one failed, the backup could be started. For present purposes these two systems can be thought of as equivalent.

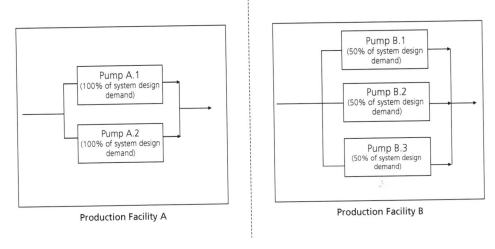

Figure 8.2: Firefighting water pumps

As it happened both facilities were to have the backup pump removed for at least two months for maintenance. That would leave both systems functioning with no backup. This raised the question of whether any additional precautions were necessary during the period of maintenance.

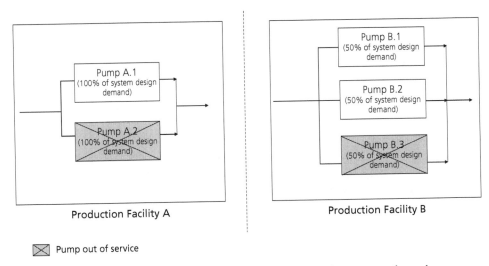

Figure 8.3: Firefighting water pumps with backups out of service

Both sites had a "management of change (MOC) standard". The standard required that any "change" be subject to a risk analysis. So, the first question was whether temporarily taking a backup pump out of service amounted to a change. Staff at site A decide that this was a relevant change and proceeded with a risk analysis. The result was a decision to hire a very expensive external firefighting system for the duration of maintenance period. On the other hand, staff at site B considered that taking a redundant pump out of service for maintenance was not a relevant change and so no further risk analysis was required. They therefore began their maintenance operation with no additional backup. As it happened the regulator visited both sites during the maintenance period, discovered the discrepancy, and shut down the operation at site B.

How could this have happened? How could the quality of risk management at two production facilities of the same company have differed so much that the regulator felt obliged to shut down one site but not the other?

It turns out that at site B, staff followed the change procedure with limited understanding of what they were doing. The first step in the procedure required them to decide whether this was a "change". Having decided it wasn't, that was the end of the matter. However, the really important question was not whether taking a pump out of service constituted a change, but whether it constituted an increased risk. Site B staff demonstrated a box-ticking mentality in which documentation took precedence over risk. If the professionals in the corporate process safety function had been involved in these decisions, they would not have allowed themselves to be deflected from the central question of whether the absence of a backup increased the risk. In fact, they were dismayed when they found out subsequently what had happened.

Two features of this example are particularly relevant. First, it involves two sites, reacting to the same risk in different ways. This could only happen in a decentralised organisation. Secondly, the regulatory intervention amounts to evidence that one site's risk management decision was acceptable, while the decision of the other site was not. In summary, the lack of oversight by central process safety professionals resulted in site B running an unacceptable risk.

Case 3: "Hot bolting"

In case 3, one of the autonomous business units in this decentralised company developed an internal procedure to carry out a particular maintenance task, without any involvement by the corporate engineering function.

At the start of a shutdown for plant maintenance, there is always a concern about potential costly schedule interruptions due to the difficulties in removing the bolts of flanged joints that have been in service for long periods and have "rusted in" (Figure 8.3 shows a bolted flange joint). To deal with this, the business unit decided to carry out "hot bolting" prior to shut down. "Hot bolting" is the sequential removal and replacement of bolts fitted to pressurised flanges currently in service. With this procedure, the bolts are removed one at a time, cleaned, lubricated and reinstalled while under reduced operating pressure. However, since the activity is conducted on live plant, it is potentially hazardous.

Figure 8.4: An example of a flange, showing bolts[1]

The American Society of Mechanical Engineers (ASME) provides a standard,[2] with requirements and guidance on how to perform this activity. According to this standard, an engineering and risk analysis must be carried

1   www.commons.wikimedia.org/wiki/File:Flanschverbindung_Gasleitung.jpg.
2   ASME (American Society of Mechanical Engineers), Article 3.11 – Hot and Half Bolting Removal Procedures. In *ASME PCC-2-2015 (Repair of Pressure Equipment and Piping)*, 2015.

out to establish that the operation can be performed safely. The standard contains an extensive list of issues to be considered, together with other prescriptive requirements. Using this standard as a reference, the business area engineers developed an internal procedure to be followed by all its facilities in performing hot bolting. However, the internal procedure failed to address relevant requirements established within the ASME standard.

This deficient procedure would have continued in place, but for an exceptional circumstance. The head of the business unit had become concerned that substandard maintenance activities might increase the risk of a major accident. He therefore requested that experts from the corporate safety department carry out a study to identify any such activities. This was not just an audit to give an overall view; it was specifically designed to identify cases of substandard practices, that is, to identify the "bad news". (The idea of "bad news" will be discussed further in Chapter 11.) A corporate safety expert duly discovered the deficiency in the hot bolting procedure and recommended that it be suspended immediately. This could be expected to prolong maintenance shut downs, at considerable cost to the business. The matter therefore had to be decided by the head of the business unit, who endorsed the recommendation of the safety expert. In this way a substandard practice was terminated. But it is also clear that, had it not been for the exceptional initiative taken by the business unit leader in the first place, a substandard hot bolting procedure would have continued as an institutionalised practice in this business unit, with the potential to cause a serious accident at some later date. If the procedure had been developed by the corporate safety department, this possibility would never have occurred.

Conclusion

These examples have involved a level of technical detail that has been avoided in other chapters of this book. Going into this detail has, we hope, highlighted exactly how a decentralised organisational structure allows substandard practices to develop. In two of the three cases the departure from good practices was so great as to have immediate consequences. To be specific, in Case 1 — the failure to flare — the consequence was a fire that seriously injured two men, while in Case 2 — the backup pumps — the consequence was regulatory intervention. In Case 3 — hot bolting — there was no immediate consequence, but the potential was so obvious that the business unit leader vetoed the defective procedure when it came to his attention.

In each case, the corporate safety group had no knowledge of the risk management decisions being made internally in the autonomous business units. *But if corporate risk departments had been involved at the outset, those decisions would never have been made.* To be specific again, in the first case, the evidence was that the corporate engineering experts were trying to *tighten* the standard rather than *weaken* it, as was done in the autonomous business unit. In the second case, risk experts would never have accepted that removing a backup pump left the level of risk unchanged; that is inconceivable. In the third case, it was the corporate risk experts who brought the matter to attention. It is critically important to make these points because they provide a basis for our claim that a more centralised approach to risk management reduces the risk of major accident.

Chapter 9
How can we be sure?

A principal claim in this book is that organisational structure is the key to safety. In particular, increasing the degree of centralised control will improve safety. What is the evidence for this claim? How credible is it?

The basis of the claim is three-fold. First, independent inquiries into major accidents or incidents frequently make recommendations along these lines. Given that these inquiries are run by experts, their recommendations must carry considerable weight. It is noteworthy that courts often give credence to expert opinion. In the end, what makes such opinions persuasive is the expertise of the people who hold them, not necessarily whether their specific opinions are supported by hard evidence.

The second basis of the claim is that organisations which have suffered major accidents respond by seeking to exercise more centralised control over risk, regardless of the additional costs that this may entail. They take the view that on the balance this is the best way to reduce the risk of disaster. Given that the costs may be substantial, the fact that companies are willing to bear these costs lends credibility to this course of action.

Third, I have provided anecdotal, but persuasive evidence of ways in which decentralised control has resulted in less than rigorous decision making and riskier outcomes. Recall the BP engineers, not subject to centralised control, who were satisfied with a well design they knew to have a high risk of failure because "the risk/reward equation" was about right. Had they been subject to the more rigorous design controls that operated in more centralised companies, they would never have designed the well in this way.[1] Recall, too, the three cases in Chapter 8 which demonstrated quite clearly that centralised control would have reduced the levels of risk.

Notwithstanding these arguments it would be nice be able to base the claim on stronger research evidence. Safety researcher Andrew Hale argues that safety science must make greater use of controlled studies in which an

---

1   Bergen, T, *Spills and Spin*, pp 145, 245–6.

experimental group that experiences a safety intervention is compared
with a control group that does not. He goes on:

> Without controlled studies, we will remain condemned to replace
> one safety fashion with another, without knowing whether the new
> is better than the cast-off old.... [We shall forever be at the mercy of]
> silver-tongued consultants or gurus selling attractive nostrums.[2]

Hale's general point has merit. Unfortunately, though, the controlled
experiment is impracticable in the context of organisational structure.
Let us consider, therefore, other types of evidence that we might possibly
draw on.

Before-and-after studies

One possibility is to take a company that has significantly centralised its
control over major accident risk and examine the level of safety before and
after the restructure. Take BP, whose restructure after the Gulf of Mexico
disaster was discussed in Chapter 5. Is there hard evidence that BP became
a safer company after its 2010 restructure? The question that immediately
arises is how to measure safety. Perhaps we might compare the rate of
major accidents before and after 2010. This means we need to define major
accident. Will this be in terms of numbers of people killed (say more than
ten)? How about total financial loss to the company (say more than $1b)?
For perspective, the Gulf of Mexico accident killed 11 men and, on latest
estimates, cost BP more than $60b.

In the nine years since the 2010 restructuring, BP has not had a major
accident, according to either criterion mentioned above. In the nine years
prior to the restructuring it had two accidents that qualify as major (the
Gulf of Mexico blowout and the Texas City refinery disaster). In addition,
BP had a number of high-profile events during those nine years, which
severely damaged the company's reputation, but killed no one, and cost
the company less than $1b in each case. For example, it suffered a much-
publicised oil spill in the Prudhoe Bay region of northern Alaska in 2006
that contaminated about 2 acres of snow-covered ground.[3] After the Gulf
of Mexico accident, these earlier incidents were sometimes put together

2   Hale, A, Foundations of safety science: A postscript, *Safety Science* 2014, 67: 64–69, order of sentences
    reversed.

3   www.nytimes.com/2006/03/15/us/large-oil-spill-in-alaska-went-undetected-for-days.html.

to create a picture of a company largely out of control.[4] But in terms of the definitions of a major accident provided above, BP had two in the nine-year period prior to the restructure and none in the same period after the restructure. Is this evidence of improvement?

To go from two accidents in one period to none in the next period looks like an improvement, on the face of it. But the numbers are extremely small, and this difference could easily be due to random fluctuations. There is, however, a statistical test, using the Poisson distribution,[5] that potentially enables us to be a little more precise. Suppose we treat the accident rate in the first period as the steady state, to be expected in the next period, other things being equal. Then the probability of getting zero accidents in the second period, as in fact happened, is quite low, 0.14 to be precise. This suggests that other things were *not* equal and that the management restructure did indeed make a difference. Unfortunately, the test makes assumptions which cannot be verified. In particular, the assumption that the accident rate in the first period represents a steady state cannot be verified by going back in time because BP's organisational structure was different in earlier periods. The result is therefore very far from being statistically conclusive.[6]

We can look at this another way. The problem with trying to use the major accident frequency rate as an indicator of safety is not just statistical. There is also the problem that it ignores near misses that might, in slightly different circumstances, have resulted in a major accident. The point is that an organisation that is lucky enough to avoid a major accident, despite one or more very near misses, can hardly claim to be safer than one which suffered a major accident when its luck ran out. Consider again the case of BP.[7] In 2017, BP suffered a string of incidents in its Prudhoe Bay operations. Most significantly there were five Tier 1 oil and or gas releases. T1 (Tier 1) releases are the largest and most serious. A T1 gas release that ignites can result in a major fire or explosion, possibly with multiple loss of life.

The first two T1s were large oil spills. The third was a 45,000-kilogram gas release in the open air. The fourth and fifth were smaller gas releases,

4 BP: Corporate Rap Sheet | Corporate Research Project, www.corp-research.org/BP.

5 www.en.wikipedia.org/wiki/Poisson_distribution.

6 For a useful account of these assumptions see Carl Danner and Paul Schulman, Rethinking Risk Assessment for Public Utility Safety Regulation, *Risk Analysis*, forthcoming, Section 3.5.

7 www.buzzfeed.com/zahrahirji/bp-alaska-resets-safety-after-five-accidents.

but took place within buildings in which people were present. Had they ignited, those people might well have been killed. BP was lucky. It was also frightened. The head of BP Alaska described this as a breakdown in operating discipline, and she stopped all work so that employees could come together and consider what needed to be done. She announced a major inquiry into one of these incidents.

We are confronted, then, with two pieces of information. BP has been free of major accidents since its 2010 restructuring. On the other hand, it has experienced near misses that in slightly different circumstances might have been disastrous. These near misses suggest that BP's management of operational risk is less than optimal. In summary, the improved major accident rate since 2010 may be a result of improved safety management, but it could also be a result of luck. All of which goes to show just how difficult it is to get before-and-after data that would provide hard evidence of the impact of centralisation on safety.

The preceding discussion raises another possibility. Could we treat the number of T1 releases as an indicator of safety for the purposes of making the before-and-after comparison we seek? Unfortunately, there is much anecdotal evidence that these numbers are manipulated, making them quite unreliable for comparative purposes. But the main problem in the present case is that it is only since 2010 that companies have been identifying and recording T1 events. There is no way, therefore, that this indicator can be used to compare BP's experience before and after its organisational restructure in 2010.

One final comment on all this. The BP Alaska experience demonstrates that BP's Safety and Operational Risk function is not infallible. For some reason, in this case it failed to operate as intended. BP needs to understand why, if it is to get the best out of its organisational structure. In Chapter 10, I shall deal further with the reasons a centralised risk function can fail.

A cross-sectional research strategy

A before-and-after comparison is not the only possible research strategy. Another possibility is a cross-sectional research design that looks at a group of companies at one point in time. Suppose we could assemble a suitable group of companies and demonstrate the *companies with more centralised control of major hazard risk suffer fewer major accidents*. This would strengthen the argument immeasurably. Again, unfortunately it is almost impossible to obtain such evidence.

Think for a moment how we might go about demonstrating the above italicised claim. We might first identify a sample of companies dealing with major hazard risk. It would be nice to simply subdivide them into centralised and non-centralised, but that would grossly oversimplify organisational reality. To progress with this research design, we need to sort these companies into order, depending on their degree of centralisation. Next, we might identify the number of major accidents they have had in some specified time. Finally, we might correlate the degree of centralisation with the number of accidents.

But there are significant obstacles to conducting any such research. The first problem is to clarify what is meant by centralised control of major hazard risk. The BP structure described in Chapter 5 is worth examining from this point of view. Its Safety and Operational Risk (S&OR) function is an organisational unit dedicated to the control of major hazard risk, as well as personal safety. The head of this unit sits on the executive committee of the company, answering directly to the CEO. That puts them on an equal footing with the heads of all the largest business units. Secondly, this function is "embedded" throughout the organisation. That means it has experts (eg technical authorities) in all the business units, whose job is to focus on safety and operational risk in these units. Third, these embedded people are primarily accountable up the functional line, not within the business unit. This means that they have the capacity to escalate matters up their functional line, if their business unit is proposing to act in ways that they believe compromises safety. In effect they can veto a decision of a business unit leader, subject to review at a higher level. Finally, this function is responsible for the development of standards to be applied uniformly across the corporation. Clearly this model involves a high degree of centralised control over major hazard risk.

Consider now some models that fall short of the degree of centralisation adopted by BP.

- Company A has a senior VP for S&OR who is part of the executive leadership, answerable to the CEO. This person is responsible for the development of corporate standards and has a staff at the corporate head office, but has no staff embedded in the business units and is not responsible for auditing the business units.

- Company B has a junior VP for S&OR answerable to a senior VP for corporate services. The VP for corporate services answers directly to the CEO, but the S&OR manager does not. The S&OR manager controls an audit team that does regular audits of the business units.

- In company C, the major business unit leaders sit on a special S&OR committee chaired by the CEO and serviced by a corporate S&OR function. The committee meets about once a month. The committee is a decision-making body and the role of the S&OR function is to liaise with S&OR people in the business units to ensure that these decisions are implemented. The head of corporate S&OR is not, however, part of the executive leadership team and reports to a senior VP for corporate services, who in turn answers to the CEO.

As can be imagined the variations on these themes are almost endless. These are all real companies and they all describe themselves as having a degree of centralised control of major hazard risk. Evidently, that degree varies. Nevertheless, it would be virtually impossible to array companies A, B, and C on a single dimension, as would be required if we were going to correlate degree of centralisation with major accident rate. It is hard to see how any cross-sectional research design could overcome this problem.

BHP

Finally, I examine a particular company, BHP, to show just how difficult it would be to specify its degree of centralisation in an unequivocal way. I choose BHP in part because the reader already has some familiarity with its structure, based on the discussion in Chapter 6, but also because I have relevant interview data.

Let me begin by repeating some of the earlier points. BHP has 3 major producing divisions: Minerals Americas, Minerals Australia and Petroleum[8] (see Figure 9.1, modified from Figure 6.2).

---

8   BHP website, February 2018.

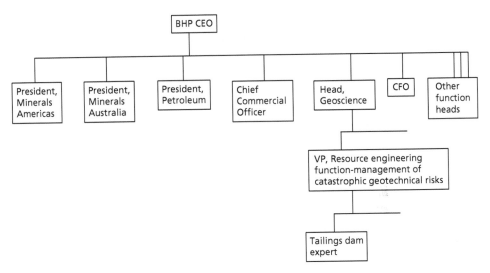

Figure 9.1: BHP top leadership team (with tailings dam function)

Its executive leadership team[9] consists of the heads of these three divisions, plus some other specialised functional heads — a chief financial officer, a chief commercial officer, a head of geoscience and so on. There is no one at this level with specific responsibility for safety or operational risk generally. The head of geoscience is responsible, among other things, for the management of catastrophic *geotechnical* risk. This includes roof strata collapse, and since the Samarco incident, tailings dam integrity. Importantly, though, not all catastrophic risks are managed by this central function. BHP has only one underground coal mine, and has decided to manage the risk of underground coal mine explosion in a decentralised way. Likewise process safety is relevant to petroleum operations, but is not seen as relevant to the two minerals groups. It is therefore left to the petroleum group to manage, without oversight from the centre.

If we look one level down,[10] and focus on the petroleum division (see Figure 9.2), we a find a president of operations, a president of shale assets and a president of conventional assets. All three are accountable for production.

9   www.bhp.com/our-approach/our-company/leadership-team, February 2018.

10 www.bhp.com/-/media/documents/business/petroleum/161212_achievingoperational excellence.pdf?la=en.

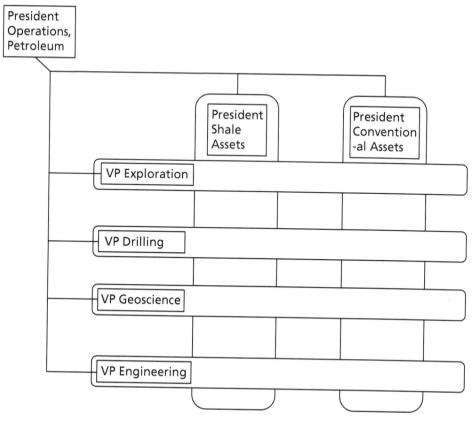

Figure 9.2: BHP Petroleum "matrix" structure

As well, there are four vice presidents, one each for exploration, drilling, geoscience and engineering. They operate across all the assets in a manner that is most easily visualised as a matrix, (although BHP does not describe it in this way). Thus, for example, the VP for engineering *"has functional accountability for all operations and engineering staff, technical assurance and implementation of engineering and operational standards across (BHP) Petroleum".*[11]

There is no one at this VP level with a specific focus on major accident risk. On the face of it, therefore, even if we treat BHP Petroleum as an independent entity, it cannot claim to be exercising centralised control over the major hazards it confronts. On the other hand, if we look again at

---

11   Ibid p 15.

the accountabilities of the VP for engineering (in italics above), it is clear that some of them are matters that would fall within the purview of VP for safety and operational risk. That is certainly BHP Petroleum's view. In its 2010 annual review, written after BP's Gulf of Mexico accident, BHP Petroleum says, in extra-large font:

"At BHP ..., we're organised for functional excellence ..."

"The depth of our functional expertise, our centralised expert services at our Houston headquarters and our common worldwide standards allow us to operate anywhere in the world safely, efficiently and with speed".

If we take these statements at face value, we can conclude that BHP Petroleum manages major hazard risk centrally.

But that is not true for BHP as a whole. Only a limited number of catastrophic risks are managed centrally. This makes it very difficult to locate BHP on a single dimension in such a way as to enable comparisons with, for example, companies A, B and C.

Even if we could array companies on a scale of how *centrally* they manage major hazard risk, this would not be the end of the matter. The next step would be to show that this correlated with some measure of how *well* they manage this risk, such as their rate of major accidents. I have already demonstrated that it is almost impossibly difficult to do this. In the end, therefore, the cross-sectional research strategy is no more viable that the before-and-after comparison.

Conclusion

Organisational complexity makes it almost impossible to demonstrate a statistical relationship between organisational structure and safety. We must, therefore, fall back on a variety of non-quantitative ways of establishing the connection. These include expert opinion, the considered judgments of companies that have suffered major accidents, as well as anecdotal evidence.

We can think of anecdotal evidence, more broadly, as storytelling. Stories about how things have worked or not worked in particular cases are very powerful ways of making a point. It is often the detail of these stories or descriptions that make them so plausible. Furthermore, whether these stories are persuasive depends on judgments made by readers, or listeners.

They are often able to bring to bear their own experience to corroborate the claims being made. People often respond to a lecture/presentation about a disaster in their industry with: "there but for the grace of God, go we". This is a recognition that the factors that contributed to the disaster are all present in their own context, and that it may only be a matter of luck that the same fate has not befallen them. It is thus ultimately the combined input of both writer and reader (or speaker and listener) that determines whether a claim is regarded as valid. The question for the reader, then, is: are you persuaded?

I hope you will approach this book in the manner just described. I have provided the argument and a considerable amount of evidence of various sorts in support of the argument. It is up to readers to bring to bear their own experience and powers of reasoning to decide whether they are persuaded. If you are a CEO in charge of a large company operating hazardous technologies, you cannot afford to wait for conclusive evidence. You must act on the basis of whatever imperfect knowledge you currently have. So the question is this: are you sufficiently persuaded by the arguments in this book to put resources into managing risk more centrally, or not?

Finally, I draw on legal thinking to support this idea. The law has developed the concept of a *rebuttable presumption*. This is a proposition that is so reasonable that it will be taken to be true, unless in the particular case it can be proved false. Arguably, the proposition that greater centralisation of control of major hazard risk will lead to safer outcomes should be treated as a rebuttable presumption. It should be taken as true, unless evidence can be provided in a particular case that it does not apply.

Chapter 10
Structure in context

This book emphasises the role of structure in determining the culture of an organisation, and in particular, the extent to which that culture is risk-focused. But structure does not exist in isolation; it has a context. Structure is heavily influenced by the dominant purpose of the organisation, which in large private sector organisations is to maximise shareholder value.

In the absence of other considerations, the maximisation of shareholder value is often thought to be best achieved by a decentralised organisational structure, as I shall demonstrate below. It is true that a disaster or crisis may cause a company to introduce more centralised control of the relevant risks, but that more centralised structure of control remains vulnerable to decentralising tendencies. The purpose of this chapter is to explore some of the ways in which the single-minded pursuit of shareholder value can undermine structures of control and, paradoxically, shareholder value. These issues have been thoroughly addressed in the finance industry, because of some widely publicised scandals. The chapter will therefore conclude with a case study of a major bank to show just how centralised control can be undermined. For some readers, extending the discussion from physical to financial risk may seem something of a jolt. But the organisational issues are remarkably similar and there is much to be learned from broadening the discussion to the finance sector. The argument is laid out in several steps in the following sections.

The attractions of decentralisation

The first step is to demonstrate why decentralisation is so attractive to a company that is single-mindedly focused on profit. I shall use BP, again, to make the point.[1] Until the end of the 1980s, BP had a matrix structure, as had most of the major oil and gas companies. All this changed when John Browne became head of BP E&P (exploration and production) in 1990, and subsequently CEO of the whole of BP in 1995.

---

1   This section draws heavily on Bergin, T, *Spills and Spin: The Inside Story of BP*, London, Random House, 2011, Chapter 1.

In the 1980s the management consultant McKinsey had been recommending that oil companies abandon their matrix structures and reconstitute themselves as a series of quasi-independent companies, in other words, that they should decentralise.[2] McKinsey argued that the greatest cost reductions and hence profits could be realised by abandoning centralised controls and leaving it to geographically based businesses to run themselves. So, for example, these independent businesses would no longer need to use the services of a corporate drilling organisation, but could contract out to the cheapest tenderer. The one remaining requirement imposed by head office was that these independent businesses should maximise return on investment. This was to be achieved by the use of financial incentives.

This kind of decentralisation was the orthodoxy of American business schools at the time. As one commentator, Tom Bergin, has cynically observed:

> McKinsey was only doing what management consultants usually do, that is to say, sell ideas gleaned from previous clients to new ones. In this case McKinsey was pushing an idea that its client, General Electric, had pioneered in the late 1960s and 1970s.[3]

Other oil companies resisted this advice, but John Browne was receptive. He regarded BP's matrix as "clunky", inhibiting decision making and stifling entrepreneurship. He therefore set about decentralising the company and removing the expertise that BP had developed over many years at head office. The result was a commercial success and BP achieved a massive increase in profit. Management experts came to study the BP model and declared it to be worth emulating. John Browne was voted the UK's most admired business leader, four years in a row.

But BP had abandoned all the checks and balances that the matrix structure provided, and in so doing it had paved the way for the two disasters that subsequently befell it — the 2005 Texas City refinery explosion, and the 2010 Gulf of Mexico blowout. As Bergin puts it with his usual flourish:

> BP had become a ticking time bomb, whose ticking was drowned out by the roar of tributes to Browne.[4]

---

2 McKinsey subsequently changed its position. As noted in Chapter 5, by 2016 it was recommending centralised control where companies face catastrophic risks.

3 Op cit, p 17.

4 Op cit, p 38.

This account demonstrates the rationale and process of decentralisation that can be expected to operate for large corporations in many contexts.[5] The situation is different after a major accident or crisis. After a major accident, companies tend to increase central control of major accident risk. Similarly, after the Global Financial Crisis, a financial disaster if ever there was one, finance companies and their regulators recognised the need for more effective central control of risk. But as these disasters recede into the past, memories fade and the immediate financial advantages of decentralisation become ever more attractive. Without strong intervention by regulators, the cycle is likely to repeat itself.

The role of bonuses is undermining risk control

In a decentralised organisational model, central control, such as it is, is exercised by means of the remuneration system — a system of bonuses. In the absence of a strong central control of risk, these bonuses play a major role in determining how risk is managed. They also have the potential to undermine any centralised structures of risk control that the company may have in place. This section examines the way in which bonuses undermine effective risk control. The following section provides a case study to demonstrate in more detail how this happens.

Although maximising value for shareholders is the primary goal of large corporations, it is not self-evident that this will be the primary goal of company officers. The literature on business firms, particularly publicly listed companies, speaks of the "principal/agent problem", the principal being the owner (or owners, for example shareholders), and the agent being the CEO (and perhaps senior executives) hired to act in the interests of the owner. The "problem" is that, left to themselves, agents may act in their own interest, enhancing their own wealth, power and prestige, possibly at the expense of owners. The way this problem is solved is by tying the remuneration of top company officers to the financial performance of the company. This is done by means of finely tuned bonus systems, recommended by remuneration consultants.

---

5   An excellent account of this process is provided by Michael Baram, Process Safety Management and implications of organisational change, Chapter 11. In Hale, A and Baram, M (eds), *Safety Management: The Challenge of Change*, Oxford, Pergamon, 1998, pp 198–199. Readers wanting a more detailed discussion of this point should consult Baram.

The remuneration of top company officers often consists of three main components — a fixed salary, a short-term bonus and a long-term bonus. The short-term incentive may be comparable to the base salary and the long-term bonus is at least equivalent to and, in some contexts, considerably greater than the base salary.[6] The size of theses bonuses is determined each year, but long-term bonus payments (and sometimes short-term), are deferred for a period of perhaps three years and finally paid (called vesting) only if certain conditions are met. Those conditions typically give by far the greatest weight to *total shareholder return*, and the condition is that the company should keep up with a group of comparable companies in terms of this metric. If the company fails to keep up with the pack in this respect (more technically falls behind the median case), all, or a big part of the long-term bonus is forfeited. Obviously, this puts enormous pressure on the top executives to ensure that their company keeps up with its comparator group. Each year, a new long-term incentive payment is proposed and deferred for say three years, and each year a deferred bonus falls due for payment. The long-term bonus system therefore contributes to the pressure to maximise profit, *on an annual basis*. It is one of the ironies of bonus design that the long-term bonus encourages the same short-term perspective as other components of the remuneration system.

The approach outlined above has several major flaws. First, a shareholder return that is a little below the median for the comparator group may still be a healthy return. Moreover, whether the return is a little above or a little below the median does not greatly affect the shareholder's circumstances. It follows that bonus designers have over-reached themselves in seeking to align the interests of principal and agent. They have done this by making the achievement of the group median a critical issue for CEOs, when it is not for investors. They have ended up creating a system in which the two sets of interests are systematically *out of* alignment.

This is not just a theoretical point. Some of the largest investors are superannuation or pension funds, investing the contributions of countless wage and salary earners. Moreover, pension fund contributors frequently opt for a *balanced* investment strategy, rather than a *growth* strategy that promises higher returns but at greater risk. The long-term incentive schemes under discussion are contrary to the interests of such investors.

---

6   Hopkins, A and Maslen, S, *Risky Rewards: How Company Bonuses Affect Safety*, Farnham, Ashgate, 2015.

Second, the need to keep up with the pack, is a strong disincentive to spending on longer term risk reduction. Such expenditure could easily push the company into the lower half of the distribution in terms of total shareholder return, thus wiping out or dramatically reducing the long-term bonuses of top executives. BP explicitly acknowledges this problem in its 2012 annual report.

> Performance related to restoring value [after the Gulf of Mexico disaster] was somewhat mixed, in part reflecting the priority throughout the company's business of continuing to embed safe and effective operations....[7]

In other words, the priority BP had given to improving the management of catastrophic risk had had a detrimental effect on various business indicators, including total shareholder return. BP was willing to accept this consequence in the wake of the Gulf of Mexico blowout, but in general the structure of long-term bonuses discourages spending on long-term risk mitigation.

A third major flaw is related to this. The risks that executives accept in order to maximise annual returns may not have any obviously negative financial consequences for a number of years. Only when this risk-taking behaviour culminates in a crisis does it become obvious that it has not been in the best interests of shareholders. The deferral of bonuses for a period of years is meant to ensure that companies consider the longer-term interests of shareholders and manage risks accordingly. But as I have shown above, there is no way that long-term bonus systems, as they currently operate, can have that effect.

Different industries have responded to this problem differently. For hazardous industries, this has led to a search for quantitative indicators of major hazard risk that can be included in bonus systems to balance the quest for profit. Various measures have been considered, but none has proved satisfactory. This is in part because there is no single indicator applicable to all major hazard risks, or even a substantial range of them. Moreover, as soon as any indicator is proposed, the first response of companies is to manage the measure, rather than the risk.[8] Most importantly, however, the weighting given to these indicators is never comparable to the

---

7   BP annual report for 2012, p 132.

8   Muller, J, *The Tyranny of Metrics*, Princeton, Princeton University Press, 2018.

weighting given to the financial indicators, and so their inclusion in bonus calculations has done little to modify the relentless pressure to maximise annual shareholder returns. This matter is discussed in detail in my book *Risky Rewards: How Company Bonuses Affect Safety* and will not be pursued further here.

The finance sector has avoided these problems by taking a different approach. The strategy has often been to leave it to boards to make a somewhat subjective judgment each year as to whether their senior executives have managed effectively the longer-term risks that impact on shareholder interests. These include financial risks, such as the possibility that those to whom loans have been made will not be able to repay them. But they also include operational and compliance risks, such as the risk of cyberattack, or the risk that the company will fail to comply with legal and ethical norms, with potentially damaging reputational consequences. Boards can make judgements about these matters for each member of the executive separately, as well as for the group as a whole. Where risk management is judged to be less than satisfactory, boards can reduce the bonuses that would otherwise be paid. Indeed, they have discretion to reduce bonuses to zero where they judge it appropriate. In theory, this should be a powerful incentive for executives to consider risk, as well as profit, in their decision-making. Typically, however, boards have not exercised this option effectively. The result has been that the voice of finance outweighs the voice of risk,[9] and remuneration systems end up rewarding financial success with little consideration of the risks incurred along the way. All this was well documented in the wake of the Global Financial Crisis, yet the problem persists to this day.

It is worth considering why boards have in general failed to exercise their power to penalise senior executives for poor risk management. I start with some preliminary comments about the social composition of boards.

Research shows that boards are socially homogenous, drawn from the same small pool of people who serve on multiple boards, in a tightly connected network.[10] In recent years, women have broken into what was previously

9   *Prudential Inquiry into the Commonwealth Bank of Australia (CBA) Final Report* (CBA report), April 2018, p 47.

10   Smith, S, Company boards are stacked with friends of friends so how can we expect change?, *The Conversation*, 4 May 2018.

a boys' club, but the social composition of boards has remained otherwise unchanged.

This homogeneity is maintained by recruitment processes. Boards often fail to advertise for new members, preferring to select from within the extended network. The preference is for people who are known and trusted. This makes it difficult for qualified outsiders to break in, and it ensures that boards consist of like-minded people. The result is that board members are reluctant to challenge each other and are susceptible to processes of groupthink.

The preceding comments apply particularly to non-executive directors (NEDs), whose role is part-time. There will also be at least one *executive* director on the board — the CEO — and perhaps another — the chief financial officer. These executive directors are of course full-time company employees. The part-time nature of NEDs makes it difficult for them to challenge the CEO, who is inevitably the main conduit of information from the company to other board members.

The dilemma for NEDs is whether to trust or challenge the CEO. Having appointed the CEO, they believe that he or she must be accorded some measure of trust to get on with the job. On the other hand, their role is to question and challenge information that is being provide to them. Achieving the right balance between trust and challenge is a delicate matter for NEDs. I have personal experience of this. A large industrial company was in crisis after some highly publicised incidents in which hazardous substances had escaped and impacted nearby populations. The CEO assured the board that everything was under control. The board chose to question this assurance and seek an external view of how well these matters were being managed. I was engaged to provide that view. The CEO inevitably saw this as a vote of no confidence. He resigned soon afterwards, whether for this, or some unrelated reason, I never found out.

Non-executive directors sometimes feel intimidated by the expertise of the CEO and the other senior executives who brief them from time to time.[11] They may suspect a "lack of candour"[12] from senior managers at board meetings, but have difficulty challenging it. All of this makes it difficult for them to perform their statutory roles effectively.

---

11   CBA report, p 14.
12   Ibid.

The failure of centralised risk control: a banking case study

The banking sector has produced a series of informative reports in recent years about the failures of boards to discharge their risk management role. Among many other things, these reports demonstrate the ways in which centralised structures of risk control can be undermined. That makes them particularly useful for this book. I focus here on one such report, into Australia's largest bank, the Commonwealth Bank. The report was commissioned by the prudential regulator, after a series of scandals which severely damaged the bank's reputation. The scandals included charging fees when no service was provided, charging dead customers for advice and providing self-interested financial advice to customers.

The Commonwealth Bank's organisational model lay somewhere between the centralised matrix model that John Browne inherited and the highly decentralised model that he created. The report describes the bank as having a "federated" structure, consisting of a federation of semi-autonomous business units, but with an over-arching risk control function run from the centre. A federated structure of this nature is relatively common in the banking industry.[13]

Like many such banks, the Commonwealth Bank had a Group *Chief Risk Officer* (CRO) who was part of the executive team, answerable directly to the CEO. He headed the Bank's risk function. Each of the constituent businesses of the Bank also had a chief risk officer, who reported directly to the Group Chief Risk Officer.[14] In turn, these business level chief risk officers had subordinates, and so on. The risk control function was therefore embedded in the businesses, in the same way that it now is in BP, in principle.

Had this structure of control operated effectively, the Bank would not have been able to engage in practices that led in some cases to the financial ruin of its customers, and ultimately to a reputational crisis for the Bank. The report provides a compelling account of how and why the CRO failed to perform his function effectively. I detail several factors below, starting with remuneration.

---

13   CBA report, p 22.

14   CBA report, p 29.

If chief risk officers are to be motivated to focus on risk and not profit, their remuneration should reflect this focus.

The prudential report on the Commonwealth Bank made the following observation:

> the CRO's .... remuneration mix is not materially different to that of the business unit Group Executives. Industry practice for CRO remuneration arrangements varies, with CROs at some other banks having a quite different ... remuneration mix than their executive colleagues, typically with a higher weighting on fixed remuneration aimed at safeguarding the independence of this critical function.[15]

Clearly, the Commonwealth Bank's CRO was being incentivised to put profit ahead of other considerations. In other words, his incentive package undermined his function.

A much-quoted guidance document in the UK gives the following advice:

> Staff engaged in financial and risk control should be compensated in a manner that is independent of the business areas they oversee and commensurate with their key role in the firm.[16]

The implication is that the CRO's bonus should have been *independent* of the financial fortunes of the Commonwealth Bank. It most certainly wasn't.

Here's why this is so important. There will always be a conflict between short term-profit goals and longer-term risk management. If the CRO is remunerated in terms of profit, that conflict is internalised within the CRO. The CRO is likely to try to balance these competing goals before offering advice to the CEO or expressing a view at executive team meetings. The "voice of risk" is thus compromised before it is even expressed. The voice that should be clear as a bell is muffled by money at the outset. On the other hand, if the CRO's remuneration is independent of profit, this is symbolic recognition that risk management should be the CRO's paramount concern, and it also ensures that the CRO has no incentive to try to balance the conflicting goals. The debate between the voice of finance and the voice of risk can then be externalised at executive committee meetings, taking place between the heads of business units on one side and the CRO on

---

15   CBA report, p 78. See also Australian Prudential Regulatory Authority (APRA), *Remuneration practices at large financial institutions*, April 2018, p 18.

16   Financial Stability Forum, *FSF Principles for Sound Compensation Practices*, 2009, p 7.

the other. Ideally the CRO in this situation can act as a devil's advocate, disrupting groupthink, and making it impossible for the group to reach a consensus view. This may force the CEO to take the final decision, without the comfort of executive committee consensus.

The remuneration packages of the Commonwealth Bank's executive officers were overseen by the Board. The Board's failure to recognise the inappropriate nature of the CRO's remuneration package is symptomatic of its failure to incorporate risk more generally into its remuneration framework.

No doubt one of the contributing factors to this failure was an over-reliance on remuneration consultants. These consultants promote a one-size-fits all approach to bonus structures. Reports have repeatedly warned of the dangers of such an approach,[17] and of the need to tailor systems to particular needs. The Commonwealth Bank Board failed to do this.

A second way in which the risk function was undermined was that it was inadequately resourced.[18] In particular, there were insufficient skilled professionals employed to perform the function effectively. The situation was worst in relation to compliance risk — the risk that the Bank would violate legal and ethical rules designed to protect customers. The resourcing issue was compounded by the fact that risk function staff were at times drawn into activities that were properly the responsibility of the business units, at the expense of their risk control activities. Under-resourcing of the risk control function is another symptom of the dominance of the financial goals over risk control goals for which the Board was ultimately responsible.

An effective way for the board of a bank to strengthen the risk control function is to ensure that when the heads of the various business units deliver poor risk outcomes, their bonuses are reduced accordingly. This did not happen consistently at the Commonwealth Bank.[19] Even where individual performance reviews formally concluded that risk reduction goals were only "partially met", the Board failed to adjust remuneration downwards. In some cases, poor internal audit reports, and even poor reports from external sources concerning the effectiveness of risk

---

17   Executive Remuneration Working Group, *Final Report,* July 2016.

18   CBA report, p 33.

19   CBA report, pp 71, 75.

management, incurred no financial penalties at bonus time. To repeat, the Board failed to hold the heads of the Bank's business units accountable for their risk management. This undoubtedly fueled perceptions among staff in the business units that the risk management function was somewhat irrelevant, or worse, a hindrance to the Bank in achieving its objectives.[20]

The Bank's federated organisational structure also disempowered the risk function. It meant that the function had no direct authority with respect to the business units. The heads of these units formed the executive committee, on which the CRO also sat. However, this was not a decision-making forum and members took care not to criticise each other. The atmosphere was one of collegiality rather than challenge.[21] It would have been difficult for the CRO to challenge the risk-management practices of the business units in this context.

There is one final aspect of the Commonwealth Bank's risk function that is relevant. As noted earlier, it covered two kinds of risk. The first was financial risk — for example the risk of a bad debt or a poor investment decision. Second, it covered non-financial risk, such as the risk of failing to comply with regulatory and ethical requirements — non-compliance risk. The CRO was primarily concerned with financial risk, yet it was non-compliance with regulations designed to protect bank customers that precipitated the intervention of the regulator and the serious reputational damage that ensued. The head of the regulatory compliance section within the risk function was a couple of steps below the CRO, which significantly reduced the visibility of non-compliance risk. The report recommended that the status of the head of compliance be upgraded to sit on the executive committee, *alongside* the CRO! The report further recommended that the position should have direct access to the Board.[22] In effect non-compliance risk was to be treated as having the same importance as financial risk. The relevant conclusion is that the effectiveness of the risk function, with respect to non-compliance risk, had been undermined by the somewhat one-sided or skewed conception of risk with which the Bank operated.

In summary, the inquiry and report of the prudential regulator illuminates the failure of risk management in Australia's largest bank, the Commonwealth

---

20 CBA report, p 86.

21 CBA report, p 24.

22 CBA report p 35.

Bank. Importantly for this book, it shows how a risk function, even one whose head answers directly to the CEO, can be undermined by a board and by the remuneration system it endorses.

Conclusion

Organisational structures do not exist in isolation. They have a context, and for a business organisation, that context is the overwhelming priority that is given to annual profit. This means that even if a company structures itself to attend closely to risk and risk controls, that structure is always vulnerable to being undermined by profit goals. There is an ever-present tendency towards the underfunding and co-option of a central risk function, in order to support the primary corporate goal — annual profit.

All this is accentuated by bonus systems that invariably prioritise profit. Attempts to counteract this problem by including quantitative measures of risk management in bonus packages have not been successful. An alternative strategy is to require boards to make non-quantitative, subjective determinations about the effectiveness of risk management and to modify bonuses accordingly. In principle this could provide a powerful incentive for companies to focus on risk and to ensure that the risk function was operating effectively. But in practice this has not happened because boards are unable or reluctant to make such determinations. The Commonwealth Bank of Australia provides an instructive case study of just how these various factors can combine to undermine the effectiveness of a risk function.

So what does this mean for the argument of this book? One way to answer this is to say that it extends the causal model. The initial model is that structure creates culture and, in particular, that a strong central risk control function will create a risk-sensitive culture, that is, a risk-sensitive way of doing things. The Commonwealth Bank case demonstrates that a strong risk control function depends in turn on the culture of the board. A board concerned to discharge its risk-control obligations effectively will ensure that the company's risk control function is operating effectively. Where a board is not sensitive to risk, the company's risk control function will be correspondingly weakened.

These conclusions highlight what needs to be done to encourage greater attention to risk. External agencies such as regulators, courts or governments need to scrutinise the way boards operate and ensure that they give more effective attention to risk. In particular, regulators need to use the powers they have to hold boards accountable. Boards, so motivated, will require that risk control functions be strong and effective, which will in turn create risk-sensitive organisational cultures.

Finally, in Chapter 1, I described *organisational structure* — the structure of positions and reporting arrangements — as a subset of the broader category of *institutional or organisational arrangements*. Bonus systems fall within that broader category: they are a critical part of organisational arrangements, although not part of the organisational structure itself. The banking industry example demonstrates that the effectiveness of an organisational structure can be undermined by aspects of those broader organisational arrangements, in particular, the remuneration system. Conversely, an organisational structure designed to be risk-sensitive is likely to be most effective when it is supported by other organisational arrangements.

Chapter 11
A way forward

This chapter begins with a brief summary of the argument so far. Its main purpose, however, is to offer a way forward — a way in which companies can ensure that their risk management function is operating effectively. I argue that the acid test of whether the risk management function is operating effectively is whether it is able to identify the bad news at the front line and bring it forcefully to the attention of top executives and the board.

The argument so far

The starting point for this analysis is that companies exposed to catastrophic risk need to implement cultures of safety, of risk awareness, of sensitivity to failure so as to minimise that risk.

Such cultures depend on having certain organisational structures in place. What is required is a powerful centralised risk management function. Ideally such a function should be:

- answerable directly to the CEO
- independent of the financial pressures that drive the business units within the corporation
- well resourced
- embedded in the business units, and
- the final arbiter of important risk decisions within the business units.

Such a function will ensure that the culture of the organisation, that is, "the way we do things around here", is one that gives proper consideration to catastrophic risk. The underlying premise here is that structure creates culture.

The main competing view is that the way to create or change an organisational culture is to run "hearts and minds" programs aimed at changing directly the way people think and behave. These programs are favoured by the culture change industry, but there is good reason to doubt their efficacy.

There are several reasons for believing that structure creates culture when it comes to preventing major accidents. First, where reports on major accidents treat organisational culture as a central feature of their analysis — as did the *Columbia* space shuttle accident report — they recommend changes to organisational structure as a way of changing that culture.

Second, companies that have suffered major accidents strengthen their central risk management functions. Sometimes, this amounts to a total transformation of their organisational structure, as was the case with BP after its Gulf of Mexico near-death experience. Sometimes it is a more limited and specific change, such as BHP's creation of a tailings dam function, following its Samarco tailings dam collapse.

Third, this book has described a number of cases in which negative outcomes can be clearly linked to the weakness of the risk management function or functions. The Gulf of Mexico accident is a case in point. The decentralised nature of the engineering function corrupted the judgment of the well design engineers. The result was that BP failed to adopt best engineering practice in the design of the well. This directly contributed to the blowout.

All this supports the proposition that structure creates culture. For companies concerned to reduce the risk of major accident, the evidence is quite sufficient to act on.

None of this is to suggest that a centralised risk control function makes companies immune from risk. Recent evidence from the banking industry is relevant here. A report on the Commonwealth Bank of Australia shows how the risk function failed to ensure that the bank remained compliant with legal rules, even though the Chief Risk Officer (CRO) answered directly to the CEO and had direct reports embedded in the various business units. One of the reasons it failed was that the CRO was incentivised on the same basis as all the heads of the business units, that is to say, primarily on the basis of bank profitability, not on the basis of how well the bank was managing its risks. The report attributes responsibility for the failure of the risk function to the board of directors, which authorised this remuneration arrangement and did not give sufficient emphasis to risk management in its deliberations. This is a case where culture — the culture of the board — undermined an organisational structure that, on the face of it, had the potential to manage risk effectively.

How, then, can the head of risk management be incentivised appropriately? There are numerous specific indicators that are useful for evaluating risk management in particular contexts. But there is no single indicator applicable to all major hazard risks, or even a substantial range of them.[1] It is nigh on impossible to identify quantitative indicators at the corporate level to demonstrate how well major hazard risk is being managed. In the next section I want to sketch a non-quantitative approach to incentivising the head of the risk function.

Learning from High-Reliability Organisations[2]

Let us first ask what it is we want the risk management function to do. We can answer this question, by looking to the research on so-called *high-reliability organisations* (HROs), that is, organisations which have many fewer accidents than might be expected, given the hazardous nature of their operations. Examples include the US nuclear navy, and various air traffic control agencies, among others.

The striking thing about HROs is that they are pre-occupied with the possibility of failure. To use a now well-known expression, they exhibit "chronic unease"[3] about how well they have their major hazards under control. They recognise that prior to every major accident there were warning signs of what was to come, which, had they been attended to, would have prevented the accident from occurring. This is true for every major accident that has been studied systematically.

A contrary view has gained ground in recent years, namely, that some accidents are "black swans". According to this view, just as black swans were unknown to Europeans before they visited the west coast of Australia, so too, some accidents have causes that were unknown and unknowable at the time. However, a proper understanding of the metaphor undermines the interpretation that has been given to it. The Aboriginal people of Western

---

1   The is extensively discussed in Hopkins, A and Maslen, S, *Risky Rewards, How Company Bonuses Affect Safety*, Ashgate, 2016.

2   For further information see my study of Australia's air traffic control organisation, in Hopkins, A (ed) *Learning from High Reliability Organisations*, Sydney, CCH, 2009. Full references to the HRO literatures will be found therein.

3   www.youtube.com/watch?reload=9&v=I5ORFsf3QpQ.

Australia were well aware of the existence of black swans. Similarly, the evidence from major accident inquiries is that the knowledge required to prevent the accident existed somewhere in the system. The problem was that it was not available to those with the power to act on it.[4] It follows that black swans are really red herrings!

Anomalies are a common form of warning sign. So HROs are particularly keen to understand anomalies and not to assume that they can be ignored until they have obvious ill effects. In the language of HRO theory, HROs have a reluctance to simplify. It may be recalled that one of the functions of the Technical Engineering Authority recommended by the *Columbia Accident Investigation Board* was to "decide what is and is not an anomalous event". This recommendation was a direct result of the Board's attempt to re-construct NASA as an HRO. Here is how the point has been put in relation to the most celebrated of all HROs, the US nuclear submarine organisation.

> One of the most amazing elements of the Nuclear Submarine culture is its self-enforced refusal to sweep problems under the rug. For decades the submarine culture has recognized the criticality of squeezing out every ounce of lessons learned from imperfect performance.[5]

HROs therefore have very effective incident/event/hazard reporting systems to pick up the warnings, the problems, the anomalies — in short, the bad news. They also have rapid and effective systems for responding to reports. In Australia's Air Traffic Control agency, reports from around the country are examined each day by head office staff. The most significant are compiled into an operations report. The corporate safety manager studies this report closely and presents it each morning to an executive briefing attended by the CEO. This group decides what follow up is necessary.[6]

HROs often have specialist units whose job it is to make sense of the reports being received, and to risk assess them, not according to some formalised

---

4   Interestingly, the originator of the black swan metaphor is not responsible for the way it has been widely interpreted. He was well aware that the knowledge needed to prevent disaster is likely to exist somewhere in the system. See Hayes, J and Hopkins, A, *Nightmare Pipeline Failure: Fantasy Planning, Black Swans and Integrity Management*, Sydney, CCH, 2014, p 89.

5   Digeronimo, M and Koonce, B, *Extreme Operational Excellence: Applying the US Nuclear submarine Culture to Your Organization*, Outskirts Press, 2016, p i.

6   Hopkins, A, Identifying and responding to warnings, Chapter 3. In Hopkins, A, (ed) *Learning from High Reliability Organisations*, Sydney, CCH, 2009.

process, but on the basis of deep experience that enables the assessor to identify their full significance.[7] All of this presupposes a level of resourcing that is seldom seen in non-HROs.

The preceding description clarifies perhaps the most important thing a risk function must do to operate effectively. It must identify whatever bad news there may be about safety at the grass roots of the organisation, escalate it as necessary, and ensure that the organisation responds effectively. This is the key to deciding how to incentivise the head of the risk function. He or she must be rewarded on the basis of how effectively the most important bad news is brought to the attention of the CEO and the board. That will require a qualitative judgment on the part of the CEO or board. Qualitative judgments enable the subtleties of the situation to be taken into account far more effectively than they can be with quantitative indicators.

A bad news reporting system

Let us examine in more detail how bad news reporting can be encouraged. It is not enough to set up a bad news reporting system and wait for people to report. Bad news is generally not welcome at higher levels in large organisations. Indeed, it may be actively discouraged. Leaders sometimes seek to empower their employees by telling them: "don't bring me your problems; bring me your solutions". Unfortunately, this means that if the employee has no solution, the problem will remain unreported. Leaders inspired by the HRO philosophy are very aware of this. For them, bad news is good news because it means their communication systems are working to move the bad news up the hierarchy to the point where something can be done about it before it is too late.

I sat in the office of a senior manager one day while she was talking on the phone to a lower level manager who had provided her with a report that presented only good news. "Thank you for the good news", she said. "But where is the bad news? I want you to rewrite your report to include the bad news." The organisation in question had a policy of "challenging the green and embracing the red". This slogan refers in the first instance to traffic light score cards. But it also had a more metaphorical meaning: question the good news and welcome the bad. The manager was implementing this slogan in a very effective way.

---

7   Macrae, C, *Close Calls: Managing Risk and Resilience in Airline Flight Safety*, Basingstoke, Palgrave, 2014.

To encourage the reporting of bad news, organisations must *celebrate* particularly significant reports. There is a famous case in the literature[8] where a seaman on an aircraft carrier thought he might have left a tool on the deck. Foreign objects on a runway are very dangerous. Accordingly, the seaman reported the loss of the tool to the commanding officer of the carrier. There were aircraft in the sky at the time that had to be diverted to a shore base. The tool was found, and the aircraft brought back on board. The whole episode involved a substantial disruption of the activities of the aircraft carrier. The next day, the commander summoned the crew to the deck and held a ceremony in which he congratulated the seaman for having made the report.

This kind of recognition can also involve financial rewards. The leader in whose office I sat had introduced an incentive system to encourage the reporting of bad news. She had instituted an award, named after a man in her organisation who had saved someone's life by his alertness to a process safety hazard. The award had various levels, the highest being diamond, which was worth $1,000. The day I visited her, she gave a diamond award to an operator who had recognised that an alarm level had been changed on a piece of equipment without going through the proper management of change process. He had written an email about this to his manager, who in turn had passed it up the line. The senior manager I was visiting had made more than one hundred awards for this kind of reporting in a period of less than 12 months.

These anecdotes suggest a way in which a bad news reporting system might be constructed. First, people must be encouraged to report anything they notice that is problematic, not just incidents that fall into pre-defined categories. Furthermore, many incident reporting systems are computer-based, clunky and discouraging to use. They require reporters to fill out numerous fields and conduct somewhat abstract risk assessments themselves. More user-friendly systems employ a mobile device such as an iPad or a smart phone. It is easy these days to create an app which would enable reporters to make a report with no attempt to categorise the matter or risk assess it. They could upload photos as appropriate and even make suggestions for what should be done.

---

8   Weick, K, Sutcliffe, K and Obstfeld, D, Organising for high reliability: processes of collective mindfulness, *Research in Organisational Behaviour*, vol 21, pp 81–123.

Bad news reports should go to the worker's immediate supervisor, as part of the normal communication between employees and supervisors. At the same time, reports should be routed one or two levels up to a site manager, who should monitor what is going on and take further action in relation to selected matters that may be beyond the capacity of a supervisor to deal with. As well, all reports should go to a corporate centre for analysis and for transmission upwards where a corporate response is desirable. This is an essential step in the process to ensure that matters that cannot be dealt with at lower levels rise to the top of the organisation where something effective can be done. A strong central risk function is obviously vital if this is to be done effectively.

Figure 11.1 shows these flows of information upwards. It depicts only the essential elements of the communication network just described. Additional lines of communication could be added, either formally or informally, depending on circumstances.

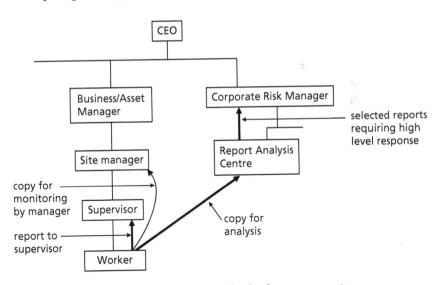

Figure 11.1: Pathways for bad news reports

Supervisors should respond to every report received, not just to acknowledge it, but also to indicate what if anything will be done about it, and why. Getting a personal response to a report assures the reporter that the report is being taken seriously. Reporters would need to be invited to respond via the same route if they felt that their reports had disappeared without trace or that the response had been insufficient. The response to the reporter should also go to a higher level to ensure that something is being done and that the response is appropriate. This whole process of responding to reports would need to be monitored closely by the corporate risk function to ensure that it was working as intended. This is depicted in Figure 11.2.

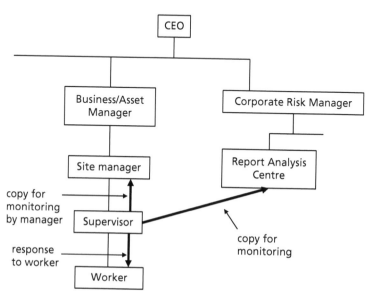

Figure 11.2: Pathways for supervisor response

Encouraging *helpful* reporting

A reporting system like this may be initially swamped with reports that are quite trivial from a corporate point of view, such as grass that needs cutting, or paint that is peeling. While these reports need to be responded to respectfully, they are not necessarily warnings that danger lies ahead. They are not the kinds of reports that will assist in reducing fatality risks or the risk of a major accident. Once the system is in operation people need to be encouraged to focus on bad news in relation to these matters. This requires a process of acknowledging and celebrating the most "helpful" report in a designated reporting period, and for some particular group of employees, say, all employees at a particular site. Determining the most helpful report will require decision-makers to turn their minds to the kinds of events that bad news reporting is designed to prevent. For example, a report that some hazardous piece of equipment, such as a pressure vessel, is long overdue for inspection, is obviously more helpful than a report about the amenity of a lunch room. Perhaps once a month, therefore, the site manager will determine the most useful report received and announce this to employees. The decision may be delegated to a committee, so as to involve more people, but it must be the site manager that makes the announcement, to reinforce its importance. In addition to this recognition, there should also be a financial reward. The most helpful report of the month at each site could receive a prize of $500 or $1,000.

Each month, site winners automatically enter a company-wide competition for the most useful report. The winner should be determined by the CEO, although again, the CEO may make use of a small advisory group. The prize in this case should be a considerable amount of money. The CEO should announce the result, together with the reasons for the decision, on a blog.

The process just described "steers" the reporting system in the required direction. It encourages people to focus on the most significant risks the organisation faces, without any need to enumerate these risks beforehand.

It should be obvious that some very useful reports may reflect badly on the reporter (think of the seaman on the aircraft carrier discussed earlier) or may cause trouble with workmates or a supervisor. To report in these circumstances takes courage. From time to time, it may be appropriate at either site or corporate level to give special recognition to courageous reports of this nature. To assist in encouraging courageous reporting, it will be necessary to grant immunity from disciplinary action to any person who makes a report and to any person about whom a report is made. In other words, the reporting system must be a no-blame system.

One objection that is sometimes made to this kind of a no-blame reporting system is that people who fear that their actions could give rise to disciplinary action might try to pre-empt this by making a report into this system. If that happens, it must be accepted; that is a price that must be paid to make the system work.

The system will fail if there are no reports, or not enough. It may be necessary in the first month or two to set a quota, requiring site managers to solicit reports from subordinates. The quota should only be temporary, however, because the system provides its own incentives to report. Importantly, it is a system designed to reward quality, not quantity. What is required is enough useful reports to drive continuous improvement, but not so many as to swamp the people who must respond to them.

Conclusion

The beauty of a bad news reporting system, as described above, is that it incentivises risk awareness among employees generally. And because the rewards are for quality not quantity, this avoids the disadvantages of bonus systems based on numerical indicators. Moreover, if this system operates well, it will contribute greatly to the effectiveness of the whole risk management function, as well as amounting to a big step in the direction of HRO functioning. It is therefore appropriate that the risk function should take responsibility for ensuring that a bad news reporting system operates effectively.

Of course, all this depends on the organisation taking reports seriously and acting on them, even when this has a significant financial cost. Suppose someone reports that a high pressure gas pipeline has not been inspected, as required in the safety management system. The reason may be that an inspection can only be done by taking the pipeline out of service, at great expense to the business. A decision to shut the pipeline to carry out an inspection would need to be taken at a very high level, and the head of the risk function must have influence at this very high level, and access to the board if necessary, to ensure that a responsible risk management decision is made. The risk management function will also need to be alert to the possibility that reports of this nature will be censored along the way and not get to the top.

It is ultimately for the board to set its company on the path to becoming an HRO. To do this it needs to ensure that the company operates in a manner that is constantly alert to warnings of danger. This means ensuring that it has a powerful risk management function, protected from the profit and production motives that drive the rest of the organisation. The board should require the head of the risk function to develop and nurture the capacity of the organisation to report and respond to bad news. And it should remunerate the head accordingly. This will require a qualitative judgement based, in part, on evidence the head of the risk function can be asked to provide.

Some boards will not be willing to take this step. I once had occasion to contact a board member to convey some bad news I had become aware of during a consultancy. Her first response was that I should pass the information to the company lawyer and not to her. I declined to speak to the lawyer and so she agreed to speak to me directly. But her initial reaction spoke volumes. She clearly felt a need to be protected from whatever it was I wanted to convey. Where such sentiments prevail, boards will have no interest in ensuring that bad news reporting systems function effectively.

As noted in Chapter 10, while structure creates culture, it is not enough to set in place a structure and assume it will have the desired effect. The effectiveness of risk management function can be undermined in many ways and it is up to boards to ensure that this does not happen.

Finally, the value of this approach is that it extends way beyond management of the catastrophic hazards that have been the subject of this book. The failure of the people at the top to access and deal with bad news is a feature of every corporate scandal. Corporate frauds — both financial and technological, for example, the Volkswagen emissions testing fraud — occur because people at the top are shielded from what is going on below them. The very best way for a corporation to avoid this pathway to disaster is to create a risk function powerful enough to identify the bad news and ensure that it rises to the top.

Index

Made in the USA
Columbia, SC
24 May 2023

17247833R00089